National Test Practice Papers

Maths, English and Science

**Age 13–14
Year 9**
Key Stage 3

Hilary Koll and Steve Mills,
Ray Barker and
Christine Moorcroft,
Terry Hudson

C000216194

The Publishers would like to thank the following for permission to reproduce copyright material:
Gunpowder Plot, Robson Books Ltd 1994

Plot Night, William Mayne, Hamish Hamilton 1977

Be Safe With Your Fireworks, West Sussex Fire and Rescue Service, www.westsussex.gov.uk

Jenny Joseph: 'Warning' from *Selected Poems* (Bloodaxe Books, 1992) reproduced by permission of Johnson & Alcock

There is no definitive version of Shakespeare's texts as many were not printed at the time. They were first printed together in 1623 and since then many other versions have been discovered. Because of this there may be some discrepancies in versions of Shakespeare used at home and at school.

Orders: please contact Bookpoint Ltd, 130 Milton Park, Abingdon, Oxon OX14 4SB. Telephone: (44) 01235 827720. Fax: (44) 01235 400454. Lines are open 9.00a.m.–5.00p.m., Monday to Saturday, with a 24-hour message answering service. Visit our website at www.hoddereducation.co.uk.

© Hilary Koll and Steve Mills, Ray Barker and Christine Moorcroft, Terry Hudson 2013
First published in 2008 exclusively for WHSmith by
Hodder Education
An Hachette UK Company
338 Euston Road
London NW1 3BH

This second edition first published in 2013 exclusively for WHSmith by Hodder Education.

Impression number   10 9 8 7 6 5 4 3
Year   2018 2017 2016 2015 2014

This edition provides support for the National Tests in 2014 and 2015 which are based on the old National Curriculum.

Cover illustration by Oxford Designers and Illustrators Ltd
Typeset by DC Graphic Design Ltd, Swanley Village, Kent
Printed in Spain

A catalogue record for this title is available from the British Library.

ISBN: 978 1444 189 360

NOTE: The tests, questions and advice in this book are not reproductions of the official test materials sent to schools. The official testing process is supported by guidance and training for teachers in setting and marking tests and interpreting the results. The results achieved in the tests in this book may not be the same as are achieved in the official tests.

Contents

Introduction

End of Key Stage Assessments

Children who attend state schools in England are assessed at the ages of 7, 11 and 14 as they approach the end of Key Stages 1, 2 and 3 respectively. They are assessed through tasks, tests and by teacher assessments throughout the year. Each child's level is reported to his or her parents/guardians and the collective information about pupils' levels is used to monitor schools.

Key Stage	Year	Age by the end of the year	National Tests
1 (KS1)	1	6	Phonics Screening Check
	2	7	National Curriculum Statutory tasks and tests
2 (KS2)	3	8	Optional Year 3
	4	9	Optional Year 4
	5	10	Optional Year 5
	6	11	National Curriculum Statutory tasks and tests
3 (KS3)	7	12	Optional Year 7
	8	13	Optional Year 8
	9	14	Optional Year 9

All children in their final year of Key Stage 1 must be assessed using the statutory National Curriculum tasks and tests which are administered to all eligible children who are working at Level 1 or above in reading, writing and mathematics. Tasks and tests are designed to help inform the final teacher assessment judgement reported for each child at the end of Key Stage 1. These assessments can be carried out at any point during the year up to the end of June.

At the end of Key Stage 2, 11-year-olds sit statutory National Curriculum tests during a week in May. Children may also sit optional tests in the intervening years.

In **Key Stage 3** some schools still use the National Curriculum tests and optional tests to assess progress and to assist with teacher assessment both at the end of Key Stage 3 and during the intervening years (Years 7 and 8).

There are two sets of practice papers for each subject in this book. Whilst these WHSmith practice papers might not give exactly the same results as national tests or assessments they can give an indication of the child's attainment and progress and highlight any areas that need more practice.

Levels

National targets have been set for children's results in the National Tests. The levels are set as follows:

LEVEL	AGE 7 (Key Stage 1)	AGE 11 (Key Stage 2)	AGE 14 (Key Stage 3)
8			
7			
6			
5			
4			
3			
2			
2a			
2b			
2c			
1			

☐ BELOW EXPECTED LEVEL

☐ EXPECTED LEVEL

☐ ABOVE EXPECTED LEVEL

☐ EXCEPTIONAL

What can parents do to help?

While it is never a good idea to encourage cramming, you can help your child to succeed by:

- Making sure he or she has enough food, sleep and leisure time during the test period.
- Encouraging your child to practise important skills such as writing and reading stories, spelling and mental maths.
- Telling him or her what to expect in the test, such as important symbols and key words.
- Helping him or her to be comfortable in test conditions, including working within a time limit, reading questions carefully and understanding different ways of answering.

Maths at Key Stage 3

Guidance for parents

The Key Stage 3 Maths Test consists of two written papers, one to be taken without a calculator and the other with a calculator, and a mental maths test. The tests will cover aspects of Number and Algebra, Shape, Space and Measures, and Handling Data.

Levels and tiers of entry

For mathematics, your child will be entered for one of four tiers. Your child's teacher will make a judgement about which of the tiers to enter your child for, deciding on the tier that best matches their ability.

This book includes two sets of practice papers, each containing two written papers that cover the most popular tiers of entry. Paper 1 of each set of practice papers covers Levels 4–6 and Paper 2 covers Levels 5–7. In each set of practice papers you will also find a mental maths test which includes questions at Levels 4–7. To gain an idea of the level at which your child is working, use the table on pages 44 and 90, which shows you how to convert your child's marks into a National Curriculum Level.

Setting the Maths Tests

Equipment needed

Paper 1: pen, pencil, ruler, eraser

Paper 2: pen, pencil, ruler, eraser, protractor or angle measurer, pair of compasses, scientific or graphic calculator, tracing paper and a mirror (optional)

Mental Maths Test: pencil and eraser

A clock or watch with a second hand is useful for ensuring that times for each question in the mental maths test are appropriate.

The written papers

A formula sheet is included for each test. Encourage your child to refer to it where necessary. Each written paper lasts for **1 hour**, starting with easier questions and gradually becoming more difficult.

The mental maths test

The mental maths test should take approximately **20 minutes** to give. Cut out pages 33–34 and 77–78 so you can read them aloud to your child. Your child should use the sheets on pages 35–37 and 79–81 for his or her answers.

Marking the tests

Next to each question in the written tests is a number indicating how many marks the question or part of the question is worth. Enter your child's mark into the circle above, using the answer pages (38–44 and 82–89) to help you decide how many points to award.

The answer pages also offer advice, provide information about common errors made by children and include tips to help your child understand the mathematical ideas.

Find your child's total score from the written papers and refer to pages 44 and 90 for information about the level at which your child might be working.

Whatever your child achieves, help him or her to feel positive and confident by giving plenty of praise for the efforts made.

You **cannot** use a calculator for any questions in Paper 1.

Formulae

You might need to use these formulae.

AREA

Circle

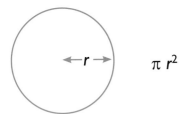

πr^2

Take π as 3.14.

Triangle

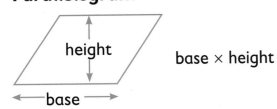

$$\frac{\text{base} \times \text{height}}{2}$$

Parallelogram

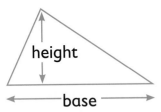

base $\times$ height

Trapezium

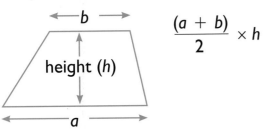

$$\frac{(a + b)}{2} \times h$$

LENGTH

Circle

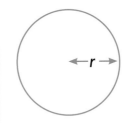

circumference $= 2\pi r$

VOLUME

Prism

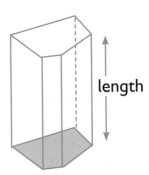

area of cross-section $\times$ length

You will need: **pen, pencil, eraser and ruler**

Practice Questions

Example

What fraction of this bar of chocolate has been eaten?

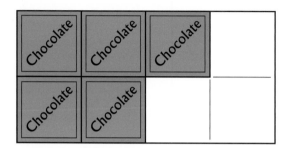

$$\frac{3}{8}$$

a What fraction of this bar of chocolate has been eaten?

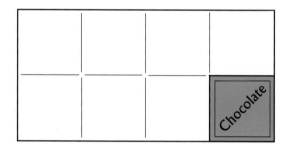

 $7/8$

b What fraction of this bar of chocolate has been eaten?
Give your answer in its simplest form.

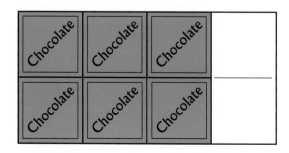

 $1/4$

Fractions and percentages

1 $\frac{1}{2}$ of this bar of chocolate has been eaten.

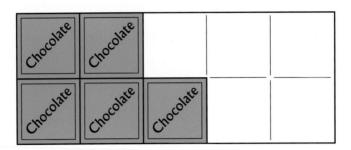

a What fraction of this bar of chocolate has been eaten?

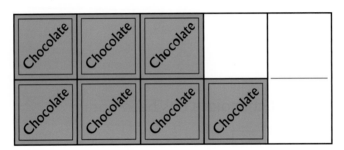

 $\frac{3}{10}$

1

b What fraction of this bar of chocolate has been eaten?
Give your answer in its simplest form.

  $\frac{1}{5}$

1

What percentage of the bar has *not* been eaten?

 80%

1

TOTAL

3

4

c Shade $\frac{1}{4}$ of this chocolate bar.

 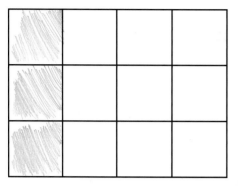

1

$3/10 \quad 6/20$

$30/100$

d Shade **30%** of the chocolate bar below.

 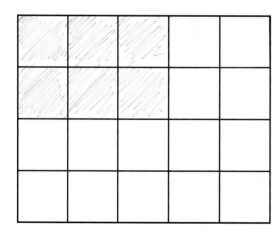

1

TOTAL

2

5

Coordinates

2 Shape A has five vertices (corners).

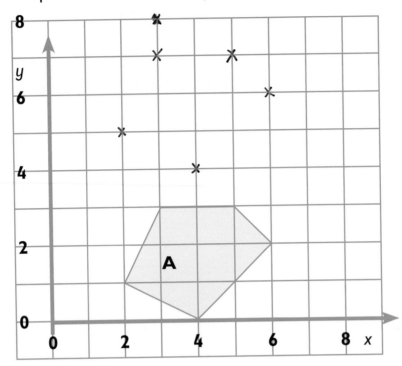

a Write the coordinates of the vertices of Shape A in any order.

✎ (4 , 0) (2 , 1) (3 , 3) (5 , 3) (6 , 2)

1

Dan has thought of a rule to change the coordinates of Shape A.

I will **add 4** to each of the **y coordinates**.

b Rewrite the coordinates, following Dan's rule.

✎ (4 , 4) (2 , 5) (3 , 8) (5 , 7) (6 , 6)

1

TOTAL

2

Now mark the new coordinates you have written onto the grid and join them up to make a new shape. Label this shape 'B'.

c   Explain how Shape A has been changed to Shape B in your own words.

Shape A has changed into Shape B by being moved up the y axis 4 spaces.

1

d   Dan has thought of a different rule to change the coordinates of the shape.

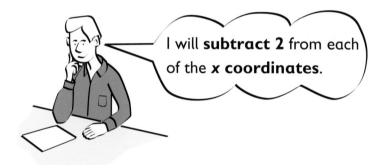

I will **subtract 2** from each of the **x coordinates**.

Explain how the shape would be changed if Dan's new rule was followed.

The shape will move left on the x axis 2 spaces because 2 is being taken away from the x coordinates.

1

TOTAL

2

Missing
numbers

3 Write one number in each box to make each equation correct.

a 270 ÷ [6] = 45

1

b 34 040 ÷ [10] = 3404

1

c [127] − 40 = 87

1

d [600] × 8 = 4800

1

e [12] ÷ [2] = 6

1

TOTAL

5

8

4   The school caretaker needs to find the area of a classroom floor to buy carpet for it. The floor measures **27 feet** by **16 feet**. This is how he multiplies **16** by **27**.

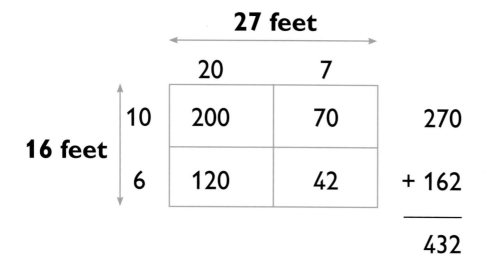

Use the caretaker's method to find the area of a rectangle **18 feet** by **25 feet**.

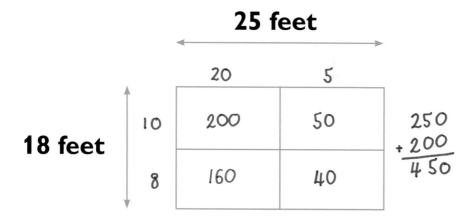

✏ Area of rectangle = _____450_____ square feet

3

TOTAL

3

Probability

5 A supermarket shelf holds three types of milk:
full-cream, half-fat and **skimmed**.

There are **8 full-cream**, **12 half-fat** and **4 skimmed milk** bottles on the shelf.
Jack picks a bottle from the shelf without looking.

a What is the **probability** that he picks a bottle of **skimmed** milk?
Write your answer as a **fraction** in its simplest form.

  ⅕

1

b Draw a cross on this line to show the probability that Jack picks a bottle of **full-cream** milk.

```
impossible              ↓                        certain
    |____|____|____|____|____|____|____|
    0                                    1
```

1

c Draw a cross on this line to show the probability that Jack does **not** pick a bottle of **full-cream** milk.

```
impossible                        ↓        certain
    |____|____|____|____|____|____|____|
    0                                    1
```

1

TOTAL

3

10

The **first** bottle of milk picked was a bottle of **half-fat** milk. Jack puts it in his basket.

He now picks a **second** bottle **from the same shelf** without looking.

d   Tick which of these three statements is true.

"The next bottle Jack picks is likely to be full-cream."

"The probability of Jack picking a bottle of half-fat milk is the same as before."

"Jack is more likely to pick a bottle of half-fat milk than any other bottle of milk."

Explain your answer.

_____

_____

1

TOTAL

1

11

Rainfall

6 This graph shows the rainfall during the first week in March.

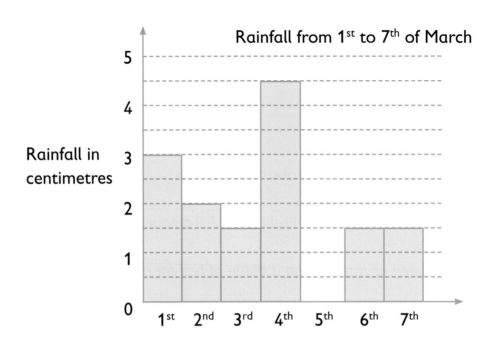

Look at the graph.

a Some of the statements below are true and some are false.
Tick the statements that are **true**.

For three days only during this week, the daily rainfall was less than 2 cm.	

For all days during this week, the daily rainfall was 1 cm or more.	

The mean daily rainfall during this week was 2 cm.	

The total rainfall during this period was 15 cm.	

2

TOTAL

2

12

b Calculate the **range** of the daily rainfall from 1st March to 7th March.

1

c The rainfall for the following week (from 8th March to 14th March) was also recorded on a graph. This is shown below. The **mean** daily rainfall for this period was **4 cm**. Use this information to draw the missing bar for the rainfall for 8th March.

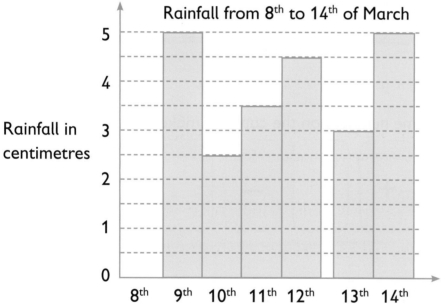

1

d Calculate the mean daily rainfall for the two-week period from 1st March to 14th March.

1

Negative numbers

7 Linford has cards with some numbers and signs on.
He arranges them to make equations.

Fill in one number in **each** equation a and b.

a

$$5 \quad + \quad \boxed{} \quad = \quad -1$$

1

b

$$3 \quad - \quad \boxed{} \quad + \quad 7 \quad = \quad 4$$

1

c Write some numbers on the cards to make this equation true.

$$\boxed{} \quad + \quad \boxed{} \quad - \quad \boxed{} \quad = \quad -2$$

1

d Reorder these cards to give the answer **2**.

$$4 \quad -3 \quad -5 \quad - \quad +$$

1

$$\boxed{} \quad \boxed{} \quad \boxed{} \quad \boxed{} \quad \boxed{} \quad = \quad 2$$

TOTAL

4

14

Equations

8a Lee has been given some equations to solve.

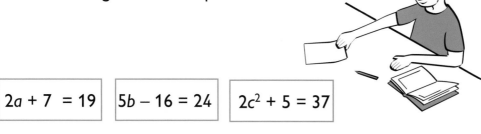

| $2a + 7 = 19$ | $5b - 16 = 24$ | $2c^2 + 5 = 37$ |

Solve the equations to find the values of a, b and c.

3

 $a =$ _____ $b =$ _____ $c =$ _____

b Lee solves his equations on a rectangular piece of paper.
The **width** of Lee's piece of paper is **8 cm less** than the **length**.

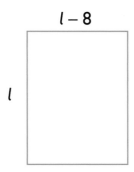

$l - 8$

l

The **perimeter** of his piece of paper is 92 cm.
Calculate the width of the piece of paper.

2

TOTAL

5

15

Missing numbers

9a Clive has written some calculations with the answer 80.
Fill in the missing numbers to make each calculation correct.

$$1.6 \times 50 = 80$$

 $$0.16 \times \underline{\hspace{2cm}} = 80$$

$$80 \div 1 = 80$$

 $$8 \div \underline{\hspace{2cm}} = 80$$

b Clive has written some other statements involving the number 80.
Fill in the missing numbers.

$$1 \text{ hour} + 20 \text{ minutes} = 80 \text{ minutes}$$

 $$3 \text{ days} + \underline{\hspace{2cm}} \text{ hours} = 80 \text{ hours}$$

 $$\underline{\hspace{2cm}} \text{ weeks} + \underline{\hspace{2cm}} \text{ days} = 80 \text{ days}$$

1

1

1

2

TOTAL

5

16

10 Jo has some small square tiles. She starts with one tile. She labels it 1. Then she makes an L shape from three tiles and joins it to the first tile to form a larger square. She writes 2 on the three new tiles. Then she adds a larger L shape of tiles to make a still larger square. She labels these tiles 3 and so on. This diagram shows Jo's shape after 4 sets of tiles have been added.

4	3	2	1
4	3	2	2
4	3	3	3
4	4	4	4

a Work out how many squares will be added in the seventh set.

1

b Complete the table.

Set	1	2	3	4	10
Number of squares added in set	1	3			

1

c Write an expression to show the number of squares added in Set **n**.

1

d How many squares in all the sets **altogether** would there be in a model with **n** sets of tiles?

2

TOTAL

5

Maths Test 1
Paper 2 (calculator paper)

You *can* use a calculator for any questions in Paper 2.

Formulae

You might need to use these formulae.

AREA

Circle

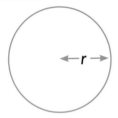

πr^2

Take π as **3.14** or use the π button on your calculator.

Triangle

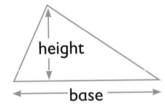

$\dfrac{base \times height}{2}$

Parallelogram

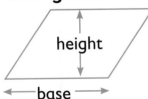

$base \times height$

Trapezium

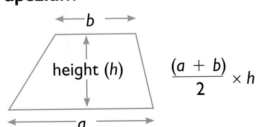

$\dfrac{(a + b)}{2} \times h$

LENGTH

Circle

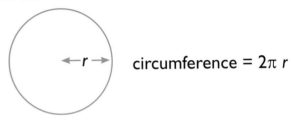

circumference $= 2\pi r$

Right-angled triangle

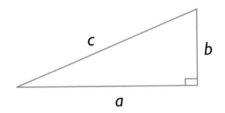

$a^2 + b^2 = c^2$ (Pythagoras' Theorem)

VOLUME

Prism

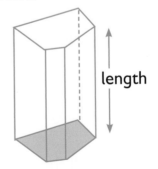

area of cross-section $\times$ length

You will need: pen, pencil, eraser, ruler, scientific or graphic calculator, a pair of compasses, tracing paper and a mirror (optional).

1 Shape A is a rectangle. Its **length** is **four times** its **width**.
Five of Shape A are joined together to make Shape B.

Shape A   **Shape B**

Perimeter

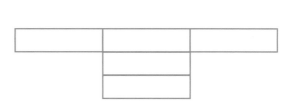

a Write an expression, using y, to show the **perimeter** of Shape A.
Give your answer in its simplest form.

1

b Write an expression, using y, to show the **perimeter** of Shape B.
Give your answer in its simplest form.

1

c If the perimeter of **Shape B is 90 cm**, calculate the perimeter of
Shape A in centimetres.

1

 Perimeter of Shape A = _____ cm

TOTAL

3

19

Ratio

2 Chris and Sam play football for a local team.

Over the season, Chris scored **6** goals for every **5** goals that Sam scored.

a If **Chris** scored **36** goals, how many did **Sam** score?

1

b If **Sam** scored **20** goals, how many did **Chris** score?

1

c If they scored a **total** of **88** goals altogether, how many did they each score?

1

TOTAL

 Chris scored _____   Sam scored _____

3

20

3a The number of seabirds nesting on an offshore island has been recorded in a table.

The number of gannets nesting has been rounded to the nearest 100 and the nearest 1000.

Complete the table.

Birds	Number nesting	Number to the nearest 100	Number to the nearest 1000
Gannet	4782	4800	5000
Puffin	5360		
Cormorant	5538		

2

b The number of nesting razorbills is **4000** when rounded to the nearest 1000 and is **4300** when rounded to the nearest 100. Write a number to show how many razorbills could nest on the island.

1

c The number of nesting gulls is **1000** when rounded to the nearest 1000 and **1500** when rounded to the nearest 100. Give the **largest** and **smallest** number of gulls that could nest on the island.

1

Largest _____   Smallest _____

TOTAL

4

21

Cubes

4   Danny has a shape made from 5 small cubes. One cube is white; the rest are coloured.

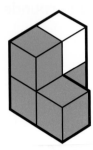

Danny decides to add one more coloured cube to his shape. Here is a picture of one shape he could make.

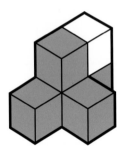

a   Sketch a picture of a different shape he could make. Shade the coloured cubes on your picture.

2

TOTAL

2

22

b Danny looks closely at this shape from six different angles. He looks from **above**, from **all four sides** and from **below**.
He draws the view from each angle.

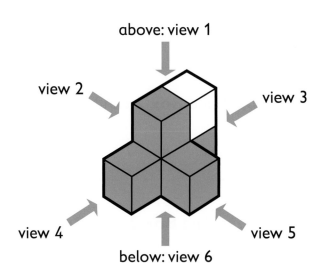

above: view 1

view 2

view 3

view 4

view 5

below: view 6

Danny's drawings are not in order. Write the number next to each drawing to show which view each is.
One has been done for you.

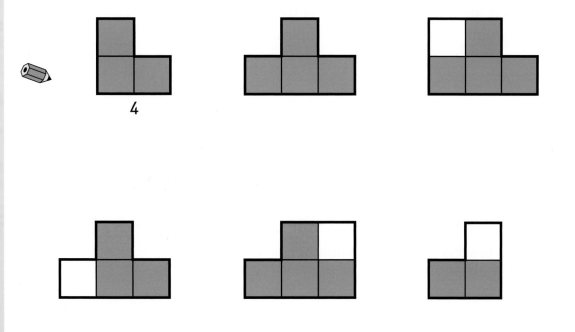

4

2

TOTAL

2

23

Expressions

5 Four boxes contain different expressions.

Box 1	Box 2	Box 3	Box 4
$a + b$	$5a + 7$	$4b + 3$	$b + 4a$

The expressions in **Box 1** and **Box 2** can be **added** to make

$$6a + b + 7$$

a Write an expression by adding **Box 3 and Box 4**.
Give your expression in its simplest form.

1

b Write an expression by adding together **all four** boxes.
Give your expression in its simplest form.

1

c Explain why the total of **all four** boxes (your answer to part b)
must always be an **even** number.

_____

_____

1

TOTAL

3

6 The exchange rates for different countries are shown below.

> **£1 = 7.60 Malaysian ringgit**
> **£1 = 380 Hungarian forint**

a Use the exchange rates above to find how much 35p is in Malaysian ringgit.
You must show your working.

35p = _____ Malaysian ringgit

2

b Use the exchange rates above to find how much 1292 Hungarian forint are in pounds. You must show your working.

1292 Hungarian forint = £_____

2

c Use the exchange rates above to find how much **1 Malaysian ringgit** is in Hungarian forint. You must show your working.

2

1 Malaysian ringgit = _____ Hungarian forint

TOTAL

6

25

Area and volume

7   The diagonals of a square are 6.8 cm.

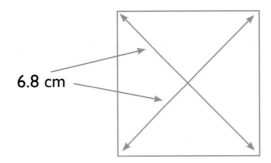

6.8 cm

a   Calculate the **area** of this square.
You will <u>not</u> get a mark for answering this question by drawing an accurate diagram. Show your working.

Area of square = _____ cm²

2

b   The square is cut in half along one of its diagonals to make a triangle. This triangle is identical to the end face of a triangular prism which has a length of 8 cm.

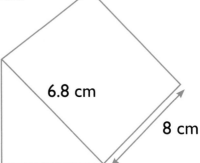

6.8 cm

8 cm

Calculate the **volume** of this triangular prism.
Show your working.

2

TOTAL

Volume of triangular prism = _____ cm³

4

8 In this puzzle, the letters x and y stand for numbers.
The totals for each row and column are given.

Equations

y	x	y	x	22 $\longrightarrow$ y + x + y + x = 22
x	y	x	x	23
y	y	x	y	21
y	x	x	y	22

21 22 23 22

Using the puzzle, write two equations and use them to find the
values of the letters x and y.
Show your working.

x = _____   y = _____

2

TOTAL

2

Area

9 This diagram shows an aerial view of a rectangular lawn with a semi-circular pond.

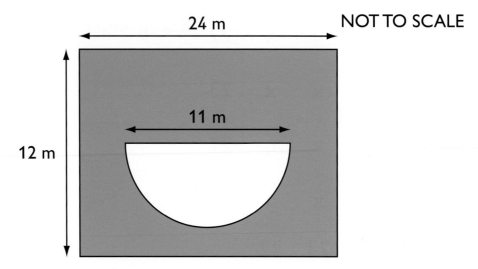

NOT TO SCALE

24 m

11 m

12 m

The **diameter** of the pond is **11 m**. The lawn has a length of **24 m** and a width of **12 m**.

a Find the area of the lawn (the shaded part in the diagram). Show your working. Take π to be 3.14. Give your answer to the nearest whole number.

_____ m²

3

TOTAL

3

A fence is built around the outside of the curved edge of the pond. The fence is exactly **50 cm** from the edge.

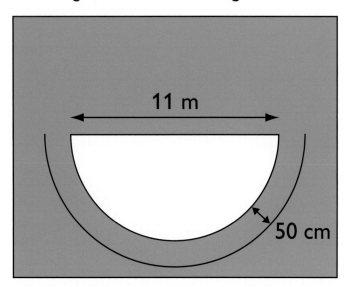

b   Calculate the difference in length between the fence and the curved edge of the pond. Take π to be 3.14.
Give your answer to **1** decimal place.

_____ m

c   The pond has a depth of **1** m. Find the volume of water in the pond.
Give your answer in metres cubed (m³) to **1** decimal place.

2

2

TOTAL

4

Travel

10 This simplified graph shows the journey of a car travelling from Leeds to Exeter, via Birmingham.

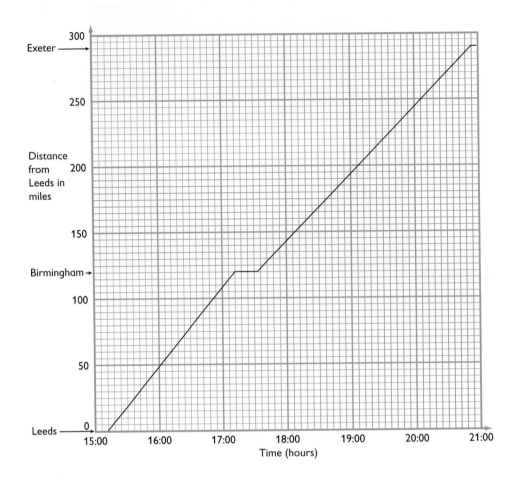

a Find the car's average speed between Leeds and Birmingham.

_____ m.p.h.

1

TOTAL

1

b Look at the graph. Without calculating, say whether you think the average speed between Birmingham and Exeter is **greater** or **less** than the average speed between Leeds and Birmingham. Explain your answer.

_____

_____

_____

1

c A second car is on a journey. It travels directly from **Exeter** to **Leeds**. The car leaves Exeter at 15:00 and travels at an average of 50 miles per hour (m.p.h.).
Calculate the time the car arrives in Leeds.

2

d Draw a line on the graph to show the second car's journey. At one point on their journeys the two cars are the same distance from Leeds. What is this distance?

1

TOTAL

_____ miles

4

31

Significant figures

11

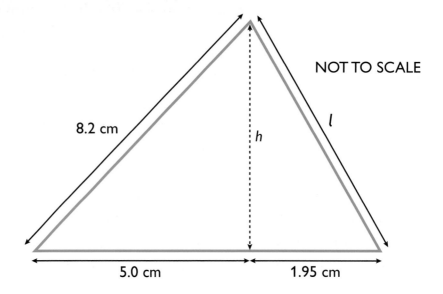

NOT TO SCALE

8.2 cm

h

l

5.0 cm

1.95 cm

a Find the perpendicular height (*h*) of this triangle.
Give your answer to 2 significant figures.

2

b Use your answer to part **a** to find the length of side *l*.
Give your answer to 2 significant figures.

2

TOTAL

4

STOP HERE AND MARK THE TEST

"For this first set of questions you have five seconds to work out each answer and write it down."

1 Write the number seven hundred thousand and nine in figures.
2 One quarter of a number is six and a half. What is the number?
3 How many grams are there in seven point five kilograms?
4 There are four red balls and six blue balls in a bag. If I pick a ball at random, what is the probability that I pick a blue ball?
5 Write sixty per cent as a decimal.
6 Change the expression on the answer sheet into its simplest form.

"For the next set of questions you have ten seconds to work out each answer and write it down."

7 If your heart beats seventy times in one minute, how many times will it beat in one hour?
8 What percentage is seven out of ten?
9 Look at the answer sheet. What is the volume of the cube?
10 Write a fraction that is equivalent to five-sixths.
11 Look at the answer sheet. If s equals nine, what does t equal?
12 What number must be added to nine point two to make twelve point one?
13 The value of eight a plus four b is thirty-two. What is the value of four a plus two b?
14 Look at the answer sheet. What is the answer to the calculation?
15 Multiply twenty-five by twelve.
16 Look at the answer sheet. Use the calculation given to find the answer to three hundred and eighty multiplied by nine.
17 a stands for a number. Write an expression that means 'subtract three from a and then multiply the result by two'.
18 Look at the answer sheet. The pie chart shows how a garden centre divides its sales area. Approximately what percentage is used to sell flowers?

"For the next set of questions you have fifteen seconds to work out each answer and write it down."

19 What is nineteen multiplied by eight?

20 Look at the answer sheet. Angle *a* is forty degrees. What is the size of angle *b*?

21 Look at the answer sheet. If *x* equals six, what does *y* equal?

22 Look at the answer sheet. Draw a ring around the number that is a factor of two hundred and eighty-seven.

23 Twenty-eight out of seventy coach passengers were adults. What percentage were adults?

24 Look at the answer sheet. What is the approximate circumference of the circle?

25 Twenty-four inches is about sixty centimetres. About how many centimetres is eighteen inches?

26 Look at the answer sheet. The cost of three items is shown. If you bought all three, what would be your change from three pounds?

27 Look at the answer sheet. Use the calculation given to help you find the answer to thirty-six squared.

28 Look at the answer sheet. What is the size of angle *d*?

29 What is ninety divided by nought point one?

30 Divide forty-four pounds equally between eight people. How much does each get?

5-second questions

1	

○ 1

2	

○ 1

3	g

○ 1

4	

○ 1

5	

○ 1

6		$4d - 2c - d$

○ 1

10-second questions

7	

○ 1

8	%

○ 1

9	cm³

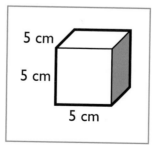

5 cm
5 cm
5 cm

○ 1

10		$\frac{5}{6}$

○ 1

TOTAL ○

10

1

11 | 5s = t

1

12 | 9.2   12.1

1

13 | 8a + 4b   4a + 2b

1

14 | 15 + (6.3 − 3.9)

1

15 |

1

16 | 380 × 10 = 3800

1

17 |

1

18 |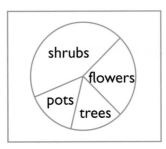

1

15-second questions

1

19 |

1

20 | b =   °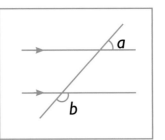

TOTAL

10

21 $y =$ | $y = \sqrt{(3x + 7)}$

1

22   7   8   9

1

23   %

1

24   m

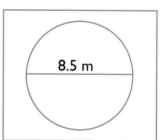

8.5 m

1

25   cm

1

26 | 47p   £1.53   82p

1

27 | $3.6^2 = 12.96$

1

28 $d =$ °

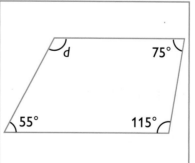

1

1

29

1

30

1

TOTAL

10

Maths Test 1 Answers

Paper 1

Question number	Answer	Mark	Comments and tips
Practice questions	$\frac{7}{8}$ $\frac{1}{4}$	–	You cannot use calculators for *any* of the questions in Paper 1. You can work answers out anywhere on the page or you can work answers out mentally. For some questions you might gain a mark for your written working out even if you get the answer wrong.
Fractions and percentages			
1a	$\frac{3}{10}$	1	Three out of ten pieces of chocolate have been eaten.
1b	$\frac{1}{5}$	1	Two out of ten pieces of chocolate have been eaten. $\frac{2}{10}$ is the same value as $\frac{1}{5}$.
	80%	1	Eight out of ten pieces have not been eaten. $\frac{8}{10}$ is the same value as $\frac{80}{100}$ which is 80%.
1c	Three of the squares should be shaded.	1	$\frac{3}{12}$ is the same value as $\frac{1}{4}$.
1d	Six of the squares should be shaded.	1	30% is the same value as $\frac{30}{100}$ which is $\frac{3}{10}$. This means that for every ten squares three should be shaded, totalling six out of twenty.
Coordinates			
2a	(2, 1) (3, 3) (5, 3) (6, 2) These sets of coordinates can be in any order.	1	Remember that the x coordinate is the first coordinate and tells you how many across to travel from 0. The y coordinate comes second and tells you how many up to travel from 0. (2, 1) means across 2 and up 1.
2b	(2, 5) (3, 7) (5, 7) (6, 6) (in any order)	1	Remember that the x coordinate is the first coordinate and tells you how many across to travel from 0. The phrase 'x is a cross, x is across' can help you to remember.
2c	Shape B is the same as Shape A but has been moved (translated) up four places.	1	If you add something to all the y coordinates the shape appears to move up. If you subtract from all the y coordinates it appears to move down.
2d	The shape will appear to move across two places to the left.	1	If you add something to all the x coordinates the shape appears to move to the right. If you subtract from all the x coordinates the shape appears to move to the left.

Question number	Answer	Mark	Comments and tips
Missing numbers			
3(a – e)	6 10 127 600 Two numbers to make equation true e.g. 6 ÷ 1. 1 mark for each of a–e.	5	Always look at the finished equation when you have written a missing number to see if it makes sense. For the question ☐ – 40 = 87, if you <u>incorrectly</u> subtracted 40 from 87 and wrote the missing number 47, you can see that 47 – 40 doesn't equal 87!
Multiplying			
4	$\begin{array}{c|c c|c} & 20 & 5 & \\ \hline 10 & 200 & 50 & 250 \\ 8 & 160 & 40 & 200 \\ \hline & & & 450 \end{array}$	3	If most of the diagram is correct but the final answer is incorrect you get 2 marks.
Probability			
5a	$\frac{1}{6}$	1	There are 24 bottles. The probability of picking a skimmed bottle is 4 out of 24. $\frac{4}{24}$ is the same value as $\frac{1}{6}$.
5b		1	There are 24 bottles. The probability of picking full-cream is 8 out of 24. $\frac{8}{24}$ is the same value as $\frac{2}{6}$ or $\frac{1}{3}$. Note that the line is split into 6 equal parts.
5c		1	The probability of picking full-cream is 8 out of 24, so the probability of not picking one is 16 out of 24. $\frac{16}{24}$ is the same value as $\frac{4}{6}$ or $\frac{2}{3}$.
5d	The third statement only should be ticked.	1	There are still 11 half-fat bottles out of the 23 left. $\frac{11}{23}$ is greater than $\frac{8}{23}$ (full-cream) or $\frac{4}{23}$ (skimmed).
Rainfall			
6a	False False True ✓ False	2	1 mark if one answer is incorrect.
6b	4.5 cm	1	The range is found by subtracting the lowest value from the highest, in this case 4.5 – 0.
6c	March 8th's bar should be drawn in to the value of 4.5 cm.	1	The mean value (4 cm) is the total of all the values divided by 7 (the number of days). The total rainfall for the week was therefore 28 cm.
6d	3 cm	1	Find the total rainfall for the two weeks (14 cm + 28 cm = 42 cm) and divide by the total number of days (14). 42/14 = 3 so mean over the two-week period is 3 cm per day.

Question number	Answer	Mark	Comments and tips
Negatives			
7a	−6	1	Imagine a number line, e.g. −5 −4 −3 −2 −1 0 1 2 3 4 5. Starting at 5 you need to count back 6 to reach the number −1.
7b	6	1	
7c	Three numbers to make equation true e.g. 6 + −5 − 3 = −2	1	
7d	4 + −5 − −3 or 4 − −3 + −5 or −5 − −3 + 4 or −5 + 4 − −3	1	Remember that when subtracting negative numbers, e.g. 4 − −3, this will result in the answer 7, the same as for 4 + 3.
Equations			
8a	$a = 6$ $b = 8$ $c = 4$ 1 mark each	3	$2a + 7 = 19$, so $2a = 19 − 7 = 12$. If $2a = 12$, then a must be 6. $5b − 16 = 24$, so $5b = 24 + 16 = 40$. If $5b = 40$, then b must be 8. $2c^2 + 5 = 37$, so $2c^2 = 37 − 5 = 32$. If $2c^2 = 32$, then $c^2 = 16$ and c must be 4 (or −4).
8b	$l = 27$ cm so width = 19 cm 1 mark for showing the expression $4l − 16$ in your working.	2	The perimeter is the distance all the way around the edge of the shape. The perimeter therefore is $l + l − 8 + l + l − 8 = 4l − 16$. So 92 cm (the perimeter given) $= 4l − 16$. $4l − 16 = 92$, so $4l = 92 + 16 = 108$. If $4l = 108$, l must be 27.
Missing numbers			
9a	500 and 0.1	2	1 mark for each answer.
9b	3 days and **8** hours **11** weeks and **3** days	3	1 mark for each answer in bold.
Sequences			
10a	13	1	
10b	5 7 19	1	
10c	$2n − 1$ or $(2 \times n) − 1$	1	The number of squares added in a set is always one less than twice the set number.
10d	n^2	2	

Question number	Answer	Mark	Comments and tips
Perimeter			
1a	$10y$	1	The perimeter of a shape is the distance all the way around the edge. Here the perimeter is $y + 4y + y + 4y = 10y$.
1b	$30y$	1	Here the perimeter is 6 short sides ($y \times 6$) plus six longer sides ($4y \times 6$) which equals $30y$ in total.
1c	30 cm	1	If the perimeter of the larger shape ($30y$) is 90 cm, divide 90 by 30 to find y. $90 \div 30 = 3$, therefore $y = 3$. To find the perimeter of Shape A ($10y$) we know that $y = 3$, so $10y = 30$.
Ratio			
2a	30	1	Chris scored 6 for every 5 goals that Sam scored. We can write this as the ratio 6 : 5. If Chris scored 36 (six times his number in the ratio) then Sam must have scored six times his number in the ratio, i.e. $6 \times 5 = 30$.
2b	24	1	Using the ratio 6 : 5, if Sam scored 20 (four times his number in the ratio) then Chris must have scored four times his number in the ratio, i.e. $4 \times 6 = 24$.
2c	48 and 40	1	In the ratio 6 : 5, there are a total of 11 parts. If a total of 88 goals are scored (eight times the ratio total) then Chris and Sam both must have scored eight times their numbers in the ratio.
Approximating			
3a	5400 5000 5500 6000 1 mark for each correct row.	2	
3b	A number between 4250 and 4349.	1	Numbers ending in 5, 50 and 500 are rounded up rather than down when rounded to the nearest 10, 100 and 1000 respectively.
3c	Largest = 1499 Smallest = 1450	1	If the number was above 1499, i.e. 1500, it would round to 2000, to the nearest 1000. If the number was below 1450, i.e. 1449 it would round to 1400 to the nearest 100.
Cubes			
4a	An accurate drawing of the shape with an extra coloured cube. Only one cube should be left unshaded.	2	The coloured cubes must be shaded to get both marks.
4b	6 2 1 5 3 1 mark if one or two are incorrect.	2	

Question number	Answer	Mark	Comments and tips
Expressions			
5a	$4a + 5b + 3$	1	For the expression to be in its simplest form the like terms should be collected.
5b	$10a + 6b + 10$	1	
5c	Your explanation should show how you can tell that the expression is even, preferably by showing that $2(5a + 3b + 5)$ is the same as the expression.	1	Be careful not to just repeat the question in your answer, e.g. by saying "It is even" without proving it. If a number is even it is a multiple of 2 and we can see this is a multiple of 2 by factorising, creating the expression $2(5a + 3b + 5)$.
Exchange rates			
6a	2.66 Malaysian ringgit	2	Divide 7.60 Malaysian ringgit by 100 to find how many ringgit are the same as 1 pence. Then multiply by 35.
6b	£3.40 You do not get a mark for writing £3.40p or £3.4.	2	Divide 1292 Hungarian forint by 380 to find how many pounds they are equivalent to.
6c	50 Hungarian forint	2	Divide 380 Hungarian forint by 7.6 to find how many forint are equivalent to one ringgit.
Area and volume			
7a	23.12 cm^2	2	There are several ways of answering this question. The simplest way is to look at the square as four right-angled triangles. The four triangles must have perpendicular sides of 3.4 (half 6.8) and so the area of one triangle is $\frac{1}{2} \times 3.4 \times 3.4$. Multiply this answer by 4 to find the area of the square. A second method (if confident) is to use Pythagoras' Theorem ($a^2 + b^2 = c^2$) for one of these triangles. This can help you to find the length of one side of the square or, better still, this length squared (the area) e.g. $3.4^2 + 3.4^2 = c^2$... c^2 is the same as the area, as c is one side of the square.
7b	92.48 cm^3 If your answer to part a is wrong you can get 1 mark if you have worked out this answer by dividing your answer to part a by 2 and multiplying by 8.	2	To find the volume, multiply the area of the end face by the length, i.e. area of triangle = half the area of the square (part a) $\times$ 8: $23.12 \div 2 \times 8$.
Equations			
8	$x = 6$ $y = 5$ 1 mark for correct answers, 1 mark for two of these equations shown: $2x + 2y = 22$ $3x + y = 23$ $3y + x = 21$	2	There are different methods for solving simultaneous equations, including the substitution method of which an example is shown below. Halve each value in $2x + 2y = 22$ to give the equation $x + y = 11$ $x + y = 11$ therefore $y = 11 - x$ Substitute $11 - x$ for y in the equation $3x + y = 23$ $3x + (11 - x) = 23$, therefore $2x + 11 = 23$, and $2x = 12$, so x must equal 6. This can be inserted into the equation $x + y = 11$, to show that $y = 5$.

Question number	Answer	Mark	Comments and tips
Area			
9a	241 m² 1 mark if you have correctly found the area of the semi-circle as 47.4925 m². Only 2 marks given for 240.48 m², rounded to 240 m² (use of π button on calculator).	3	To find the area of the lawn, first find the area of the pond: Area of a circle = πr^2 (÷ 2 as it is a semi-circle). Area of pond = $\pi \times 5.5^2 \div 2$ = 47.4925 m². Subtract this from the area of the rectangle (12 × 24 = 288 m²) 288 – 47.4925 = 240.5075 m². NOTE: *If you have used the π button on your calculator your answers will be different. The question stated that π should be taken as 3.14.*
9b	1.6 m 1 mark for the answer 3.2 (twice the correct answer).	2	Circumference = $2\pi r$ or πd Length of curved edge of semi-circle = 11 × π ÷ 2 Length of fence = 12 × π ÷ 2 The difference is found by subtracting one from the other.
9c	47.5 m³ 1 mark if your answer is the same number as you gave for the area of the pond calculated in part a, but given in m³.	2	The volume is depth multiplied by the area of the surface, i.e. the area of the semi-circle.
Travel			
10a	60 m.p.h.	1	The car travels 120 miles in two hours, so 60 miles in one hour.
10b	Your answer must show that you've noticed that the gradient (slope) is steeper for the first part of the graph so the average speed between Birmingham and Exeter must be **less** than between Leeds and Birmingham.	1	The steeper the gradient, the faster the speed; in other words, the car travels more miles in a shorter time.
10c	20:48 1 mark for the number 5.8 in your working.	2	It would take the car 5.8 hours. This is found by dividing 290 miles by 50 m.p.h. 0.8 hours is 48 minutes. This can be found by multiplying 0.8 × 60 = 48. So the journey would take 5 hours and 48 minutes.
10d	140 miles	1	The point where your two lines should cross.
Significant figures			
11a	6.5 cm 1 mark if your answer has more than 2 digits, e.g. 6.499	2	Use Pythagoras' Theorem ($a^2 + b^2 = c^2$). $5^2 + h^2 = 8.2^2$ so $h^2 = 8.2^2 - 5^2$ $h^2 = 42.24$, therefore h = 6.49923 cm.
11b	6.8 cm 1 mark if your answer has more than 2 digits, e.g. 6.785	2	Use your answer to part a and Pythagoras' Theorem ($a^2 + b^2 = c^2$). $1.95^2 + 6.5^2 = l^2$ $l^2 = 46.0525$, therefore l = 6.786199 cm. (or $1.95^2 + 42.24 = l^2$, l = 6.785462 cm).

Mental Maths Test 1

Answers

One mark per correct answer.

1. 700 009
2. 26
3. 7500 g
4. $\frac{3}{5}$ or equivalent e.g. $\frac{6}{10}$
5. 0.6
6. $3d - 2c$
7. 4200
8. 70%
9. 125 cm^3
10. any fraction equivalent to $\frac{5}{6}$ e.g. $\frac{10}{12}$
11. 45
12. 2.9
13. 16
14. 17.4
15. 300
16. 3420
17. $2(a - 3)$
18. approx. 25%
19. 152
20. 140°
21. 5
22. 7
23. 40%
24. approx. 26 m
25. 45 cm
26. 18p
27. 1296
28. 115°
29. 900
30. £5.50

National Curriculum Levels

Maths Test 1

Write your scores below.

Mark scored in Paper 1   [ ]   out of 45

Mark scored in Paper 2   [ ]   out of 45

Mark scored in Mental Maths Test   [ ]   out of 30

Total score   [ ]   out of 120

Use this table to find what level you might be working at.

Mark	0–16	17–32	33–65	66–100	101–110	111–120
Level	3	4	5	6	7	8

You *cannot* use a calculator for any questions in Paper 1.

Formulae

You might need to use these formulae.

AREA

Circle

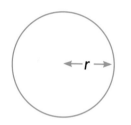

πr^2

Take π as 3.14.

Triangle

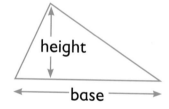

$\dfrac{base \times height}{2}$

Parallelogram

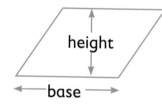

$base \times height$

Trapezium

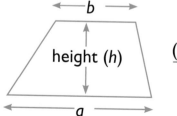

$\dfrac{(a + b)}{2} \times h$

LENGTH

Circle

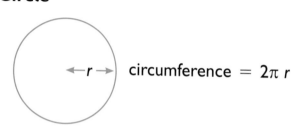

circumference $= 2\pi r$

VOLUME

Prism

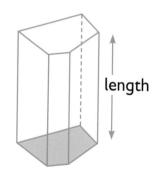

area of cross-section $\times$ length

You will need: pen, pencil, eraser, ruler

Practice Questions

Write one number in each box to make each equation correct.

Example

$$144 + 30 = \boxed{\textbf{174}}$$

a   168 + 40 = $\boxed{}$

b   835 − 40 = $\boxed{}$

c   100 − $\boxed{}$ = 72

d   10 × $\boxed{}$ = 420

Calculations

1 Write one number in each box to make each equation correct.

a **39 ×** ☐ **= 39 000**

1

b **1000 ÷** ☐ **= 4**

1

c ☐ **− 50 = 97**

1

d ☐ **× 6 = 480**

1

e ☐ **÷** ☐ **= 16**

1

TOTAL

5

Diagonals

2 Diagonals join opposite vertices. A square has diagonals that are equal in length and which bisect each other. (If two lines bisect each other they cross at their midpoints.)

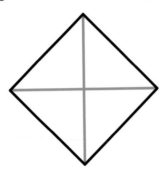

Here are some quadrilaterals.

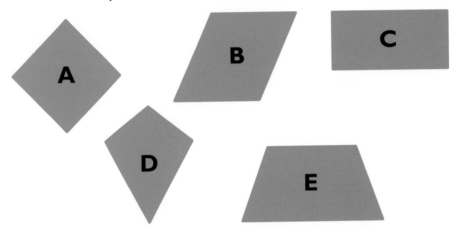

Write 'yes' or 'no' in each box to complete the table below.

	Diagonals equal?	Diagonals bisect each other?
Shape A	yes	yes
Shape B		
Shape C		
Shape D		
Shape E		

4

TOTAL

4

48

3   In a shop, some lengths of cane are being measured with a
    metre stick. Here are three canes labelled A, B and C.

1 metre

A

B

C

a   What fraction of a metre is Cane A?

1

b   What fraction of a metre is Cane B?
        Give your answer in its simplest form.

1

c   What percentage of a metre is Cane C?

1

TOTAL

3

49

d Another cane, Cane D, is exactly $\frac{2}{5}$ of a metre.

Give the length of Cane D in centimetres.

1

 Cane D = _____ cm

e Mr Kumar buys 10 pieces of **Cane A**.
If these canes were placed end-to-end in a straight line, how long
would the line be?

1

f Another cane, Cane E, is $\frac{2}{3}$ of a metre.

One of the statements below is true. Tick the true statement.

1

Cane E is shorter than Cane B.	
Cane E is longer than Cane C.	
Cane E is longer than Cane B but shorter than Cane C.	
Cane E is shorter than Cane B but longer than Cane A.	

TOTAL

3

4a A teacher collects money from pupils for a school residential trip. Each pupil pays **12** instalments of **£8.50**.
What is the total amount of money each pupil pays for the trip?

Money

1

 £

b Each pupil takes exactly **£25** spending money on the school trip.
There are **40** pupils.
How much spending money do the pupils take in total?

1

 £

c **30** pupils each buy an ice cream.
The ice creams cost **99p**.
How much money do they spend on ice creams in total?

1

 £

TOTAL

3

d Ged spends **£4.49** on a T-shirt.
He pays with a **£20** note.
How much change does he get?

1

e Claire writes down how much she spent while on the trip.

Ice creams	**£3.96**
T-shirt	**£4.49**
Cap	**£2.50**
Sweets	**86p**

How much did she spend in total?

 £

1

TOTAL

2

52

5   A bag of money contains different coins.

It has **five 20p** coins, **four 10p** coins, **two 5p** coins and a **1p coin**.

a   What is the **probability** that one coin picked from the bag at random is a **1p**? Write your answer as a **fraction**.

1

b   Draw a cross on this line to show the probability that the coin is a 10p.

1

c   Draw a cross on this line to show the probability that the coin is not a 5p.

1

1

d Draw a cross on this line to show the probability that the coin is a silver coin.

impossible   certain

0   1

Davina decides to pick a coin, record it and **put the coin back**. She does this **30 times**. She organises her results into a table.

Coin	Frequency
20p	12
10p	7
5p	8
1p	3

e Davina looks at her results and says:

"There is a greater probability of picking a 5p coin than a 10p."

Explain why Davina is **wrong**.

_____

_____

_____

1

TOTAL

2

54

6 Sam has some tropical fish in a tank.

Call the number of fish he has **n**.

Sam puts 4 more fish into the tank.

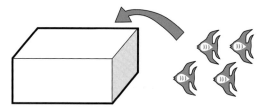

a Write an expression to show how many fish are now in the tank.

_____

1

b Sam takes the new fish out so that he starts again with **n** fish in his tank.

He takes out exactly **one-half** of the fish in the tank and puts them into a bowl.

Write an expression to show how many fish are now in the tank.

1

_____

TOTAL

2

Sam starts again with **n** fish in the tank.

c Write an expression to show how many fish Sam would have if he had **double** this number of fish.

d Sam's dad has exactly **20 times** as many fish as Sam has. Write an expression to show how many fish Sam's dad has.

e These expressions show how many fish are in these two tanks.

Tank A	Tank B
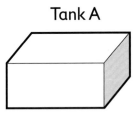	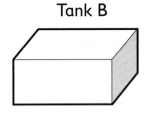
$3n - 3$	$3(n - 3)$

Do the tanks hold the same number?
Explain your answer.

1

1

1

TOTAL

3

7   Here is a sequence of shapes made from white and coloured triangles.

 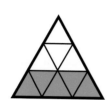 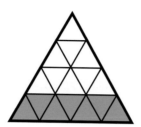 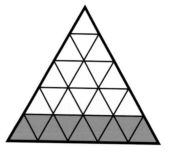

Shape 1   Shape 2   Shape 3   Shape 4

a Complete the table by filling in the missing numbers for Shape **7** and Shape **10**.

Shape number	1	2	3	4	7	10
Number of coloured triangles	3	5	7	9		
Number of white triangles	1	4	9	16		

2

b Complete the table by writing **expressions** for Shape **n**.

Shape number	1	2	3	4	n
Number of coloured triangles	3	5	7	9	
Number of white triangles	1	4	9	16	

2

TOTAL

4

57

1

c Write an expression to show the **total** number of triangles used to make Shape **n**.

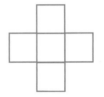 _____

1

d For a different sequence of shapes, the number of **squares** used can be expressed as **2n + 3**.

Which of the sets of shapes below shows Shapes 1 and 2 in this sequence?

Set 1

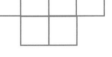

Shape 1   Shape 2

Set 2

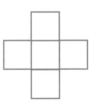   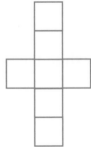

Shape 1   Shape 2

Set 3

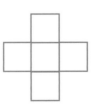   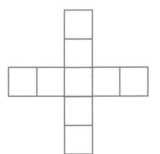

Shape 1   Shape 2

TOTAL

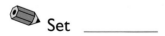 Set _____

2

8 This shape is part of a design. The line AB is parallel to DE.

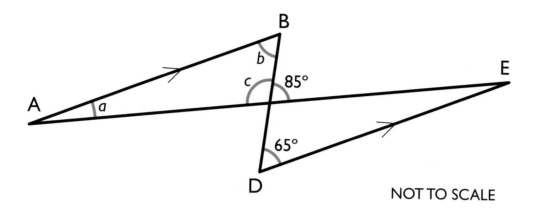

NOT TO SCALE

Calculate angles *a*, *b* and *c*.

a = _____ °

3

b = _____ °

c = _____ °

TOTAL

3

59

9 Aswin has been plotting some lines on a graph.
The line AB is **parallel** to the line DE.

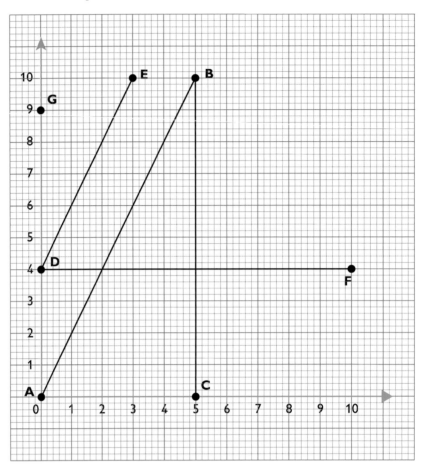

a The equation of the line DF is $y = 4$.
What is the equation of the line BC?

1

b The line AB has the equation $y = 2x$.
What is the equation of the line DE?

1

c A line that is parallel to the line AB passes through the point
G(0, 9). What is the equation of that line?

1

TOTAL

3

10 Here are two shapes.
The area of the trapezium is **three times** the area of the
parallelogram.

Areas

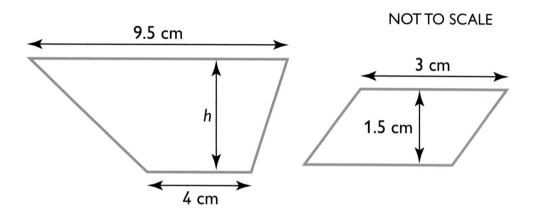

NOT TO SCALE

9.5 cm

h

4 cm

3 cm

1.5 cm

a Calculate the height of the trapezium *(h)*.
Show your working.

2

h = _____ cm

b What is the area of the trapezium below?
Give your answer in terms of *y*, in its simplest form.

1

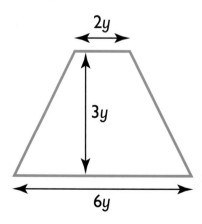

2y

3y

6y

 Area = _____

TOTAL

3

You *can* use a calculator for any questions in Paper 2.

Formulae

You might need to use these formulae.

AREA

Circle

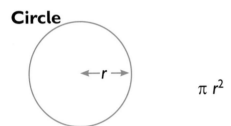

πr^2

Take π as **3.14** or use the π button on your calculator.

Triangle

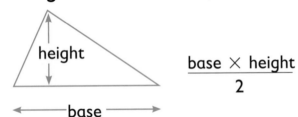

$\dfrac{\text{base} \times \text{height}}{2}$

Parallelogram

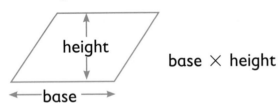

base $\times$ height

Trapezium

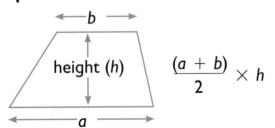

$\dfrac{(a + b)}{2} \times h$

LENGTH

Circle

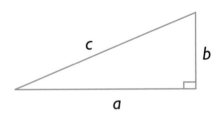

circumference $= 2\pi r$

Right-angled triangle

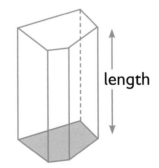

$a^2 + b^2 = c^2$ (Pythagoras' Theorem)

VOLUME

Prism

area of cross-section $\times$ length

You will need: pen, pencil, eraser, ruler, scientific or graphic calculator, a pair of compasses, protractor, tracing paper, mirror (optional).

1 This graph shows the progress of two runners during a 60-metre race.

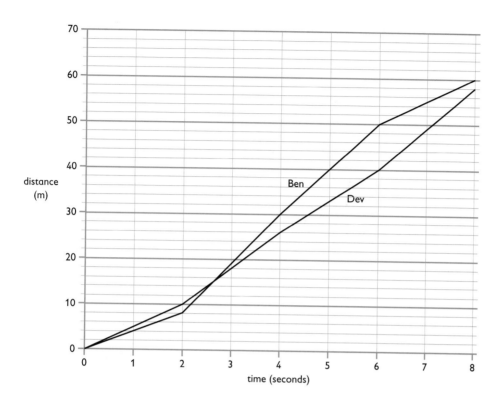

Running rates

a This table shows the progress of **Dev** during the race.
Complete the table, using the graph above.

Time interval (s)	Distance at start (m)	Distance at end (m)	Distance covered (m)
0–2	0	10	10
2–4	10	26	16
4–6			
6–8			

2

TOTAL

2

63

This table shows the progress of **Ben** during the race.

Time interval (s)	Distance at start (m)	Distance at end (m)	Distance covered (m)
0–2	0	8	8
2–4	8	30	22
4–6	30	50	20
6–8	50	60	10

b Use the two tables to help you describe the differences in progress between the two runners during the race.

_____

_____

_____

_____

2

c Use the graph to see which of the runners won the 60-metre race.

1

TOTAL

3

_____

2   Here is a sequence of shapes made from white and coloured squares.

Shape 1   Shape 2   Shape 3   Shape 4

> The rule for finding the **number of squares** in **Shape *n*** is
>
> **3*n* + 2**

a   Venus says:

"You can see that the pattern is 3n + 2 by studying the shapes."

Explain in your own words what you think Venus means.

_____

_____

_____

1

b   How many **white** squares and how many **coloured** squares are in Shape 12?

_____ white and _____ coloured squares

2

TOTAL

3

65

c A shape in this sequence is made from **62** squares. What is the number of this shape?

 Shape _____

d Here is a new sequence of shapes made from white and coloured squares.

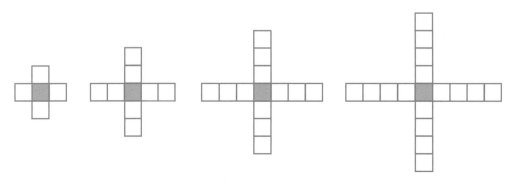

Shape 1   Shape 2   Shape 3   Shape 4

Write a rule for finding the number of squares in **Shape n**.

Number of squares =

1

1

TOTAL

2

3   Here are two shapes made from small cubes. Three of the cubes are coloured.

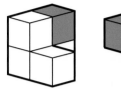

The two shapes are joined together to make a **cuboid**.

a   Draw a picture of this **cuboid** on the grid below.
Shade the three coloured cubes on your picture.

2

b   Each small cube is one centimetre cubed (1 cm³).
Write the dimensions of the cuboid you have drawn.

 Length = _____ cm   Width = _____ cm   Height = _____ cm

1

TOTAL

3

Here is a drawing of a different cuboid made from centimetre cubes.

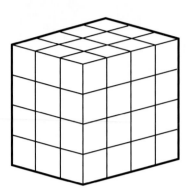

c   What is the **volume** of this cuboid?

2

Volume = _____ cm³

d   Jo picks up this cuboid. She looks at it from all angles. She realises that some of the small cubes inside the cuboid cannot be seen from any angle.

How many of the small cubes **cannot** be seen?

1

_____

e   What fraction of the total number of cubes **can** be seen?

1

TOTAL

4

_____

4 Jeremy knows that the volume of a cuboid is **430.68 cm³**.
He knows that the height is 12 cm, and that the length is
6 cm greater than the width.

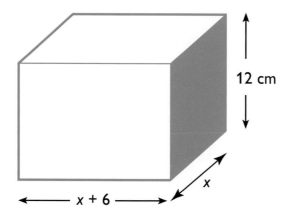

12 cm

x

$x + 6$

Jeremy writes this equation to show the volume of the cuboid.

$x (x + 6) \times 12 = 430.68$

Find the value of x.

You may find this table helpful.

x	$x + 6$	$x (x + 6)$	$x (x + 6) \times 12$	
4	10	40	480	too large

4

 $x =$ _____ cm

TOTAL

4

Ratio

5 When baking cakes, Rob follows this instruction:

| **4 parts butter** to **3 parts flour** |

a In one cake, Rob uses **360 g** of **flour**.
How much butter does he use?

 butter = _____ g

1

b In a second cake, Rob uses **160 g** of **butter**.
How much flour does he use?

 flour = _____ g

1

c Rob makes a third cake. He mixes a total of **3500 g** of **flour and butter**.
How much **flour and butter** does he use?
Show your working.

2

TOTAL

flour = _____ g   butter = _____ g

4

6 This sketch shows the measurements of a scalene triangle.
Angle *a* is not given.

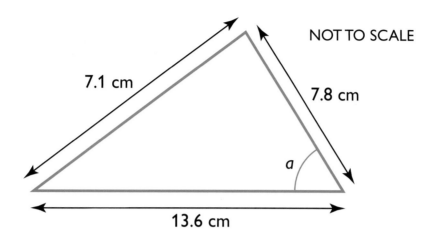

7.1 cm

NOT TO SCALE

7.8 cm

a

13.6 cm

a Make an **accurate** full-size drawing of the triangle.
You may use a ruler and a pair of compasses.

2

b Use a protractor to measure angle *a* in your drawing, to the
nearest degree.

1

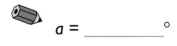
a = _____ °

TOTAL

3

7a The **diameter** of a circle is **24 cm**.

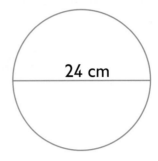

24 cm

Find the **area** of this circle. Take π to be 3.14.
Show your working.

Area of circle = _____ cm²

2

b The **circumference** of a different circle is **88 cm** to the nearest centimetre.
Find the **radius** of this circle.
Give your answer to the nearest centimetre.
Show your working.

Radius of circle = _____ cm

2

TOTAL

4

8 During Sports Day some students took part in the cricket ball throwing competition. Their results are shown below.

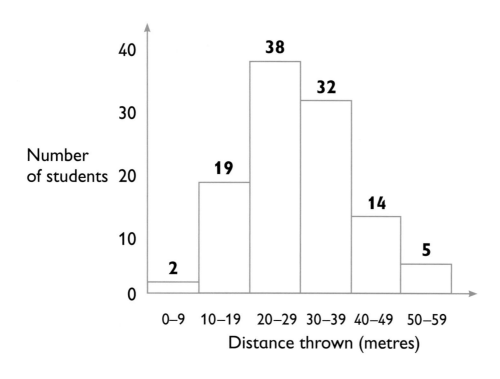

a How many students took part in the competition?

_____

1

b Serena says:

" Less than half of the students threw further than 25 metres."

Do you think Serena's comment is true or false, or do you think more information is needed? Explain your answer.

_____

_____

1

_____

TOTAL

2

73

c Tanya says:

"The range of the throws is 59 m."

Do you think Tanya's comment is true or false, or do you think more information is needed? Explain your answer.

_____

_____

_____

1

d Calculate an estimate of the **mean** distance thrown.
Give your answer to 1 decimal place.
You may find this table helpful.

Metres	Midpoint of bar (x)	Number of students (f)	fx
0–9	4.5	2	9
10–19	14.5	19	
20–29	24.5	38	
30–39	34.5	32	
40–49	44.5	14	
50–59	54.5	5	

_____ m

2

TOTAL

3

9 The heights of Anne (*a*), Brian (*b*), Caz (*c*) and Darren (*d*) are measured in centimetres. These equations show some information about their heights.

Heights

$c = 140$

$b - c = 40$

$b + c = a + d$

$$\frac{a + b + c + d}{4} = 160$$

$a = 165$

Use these equations to work out whether each of these statements is true or false.

Caz is taller than Brian.

 ☐ True   ☐ False

1

The sum of Anne's and Darren's heights is 320 cm.

 ☐ True   ☐ False

1

The mean height of the 4 people is 160 cm.

 ☐ True   ☐ False

1

Darren is taller than Anne.

 ☐ True   ☐ False

1

TOTAL

4

Field

10 Andy and Carol are out walking. They reach a field where a sign says 'Beware of the bull!' Instead of walking across the field, they decide to walk around the edge.

The field is rectangular with a width of 28 m and a length of 35 m.

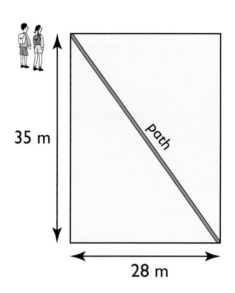

35 m

Path

28 m

How much further do they walk around the edge than they would walk straight across the field?
Show your working. Give your answer to 2 significant figures.

4

"For this first set of questions you have five seconds to work out each answer and write it down."

1 Write nought point three recurring as a fraction.

2 Look at your answer sheet. What is half the total of the numbers shown?

3 What is three thousand five hundred multiplied by ten?

4 How many grams are there in two point five kilograms?

5 Look at your answer sheet. Change the fraction into its simplest form.

6 Write the number thirty-two point eight three to one decimal place.

"For the next set of questions you have ten seconds to work out each answer and write it down."

7 Look at the answer sheet. What is the value of p when q equals ten?

8 Six out of twenty-five goals scored in the Premier League last week were scored in the second half. What percentage of goals were scored in the second half?

9 Look at the answer sheet. What is the area of the triangle?

10 The ratio of adults to children at the swimming pool was two to five. If there were eight adults, how many children were there?

11 Write two numbers with a difference of eight point six two.

12 Write a fraction that is equivalent to six-sevenths.

13 In the high jump, Dan's first jump was one point three metres. His second jump was one point five seven metres. How many centimetres higher was his second jump?

14 Look at the answer sheet. What is the value of ten y?

15 The mean of three numbers is five. Two of the numbers are three and four. What is the third number?

16 Look at the answer sheet. Which number is nearest to one and a half?

17 The value of four a plus three b is twelve. What is the value of eight a plus six b?

18 Look at the answer sheet. Write a possible value for s.

"For the next set of questions you have fifteen seconds to work out each answer and write it down."

19 The difference between *c* and *d* is four. The product of *c* and *d* is forty-five. What are the values of *c* and *d*?

20 Look at the pie chart on the answer sheet. Thirty-six people said where they went on holiday last year. About how many more people went on holiday to Britain than France?

21 What is half of five-eighths?

22 Write three odd numbers that add up to thirty-three.

23 Look at the answer sheet. Use the calculation to help you to answer the question.

24 Look at the answer sheet. The area of the square is *n* squared. What is its perimeter?

25 A megaburger costs one pound forty-nine pence. What would five megaburgers cost?

26 Divide six hundred and seventy-five by seventy-five.

27 Look at the answer sheet. Draw a ring around the largest expression.

28 Look at the answer sheet. The length of this pool is twice the width. The perimeter is eighteen metres. What is the length of the pool?

29 What is two to the power four divided by four?

30 Look at the answer sheet. Write an expression, in terms of *y*, for *z* plus two.

5-second questions

1

⬤ 1

2 | 23   27

⬤ 1

3

⬤ 1

4   grams

⬤ 1

5 | $\dfrac{16}{24}$

⬤ 1

6 | 32.83

⬤ 1

10-second questions

7 | $p =$ | $4p = q$

⬤ 1

8   %

⬤ 1

9   cm^2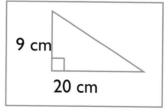

⬤ 1

10

⬤ 1

TOTAL

⬤ 10

1	11	8.62
1	12	$\dfrac{6}{7}$
1	13 centimetres	
1	14	$2y = 9$
1	15	
1	16	1.4 1.59 1.6 1.42
1	17	$4a + 3b$ $8a + 6b$
1	18	$-1 < s < 1$

15-second questions

1	19 and	
1	20	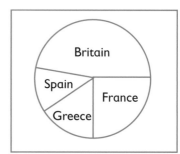

TOTAL

10

80

21 | | 1

22 | | 1

23 | $32 \times 1.6 =$ | $32 \times 16 = 512$ | 1

24 | | area = n^2 | 1

25 | £ | 1

26 | | 1

27 | $8^2 - 20$ 6^2 $5^2 + 4^2$ | 1

28 | metres | 1

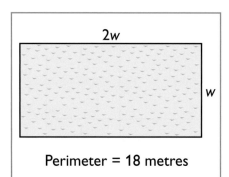

Perimeter = 18 metres

29 | | 1

30 | | $y - 4 = z$ | 1

TOTAL

10

Maths Test 2 Answers

Paper 1

Question number	Answer	Mark	Comments and tips
Practice questions	208 795 28 42	–	You cannot use calculators for *any* of the questions in Paper 1. You can work answers out anywhere on the page or you can work answers out mentally. For some questions you might gain a mark for your written working out even if you get the answer wrong.
Calculations			
1a b c d e	1000 250 147 80 Two numbers to make equation true e.g. 32, 2.	5	Always look at the finished equation when you have written a missing number to see if it makes sense. For the question $\boxed{}$ – 50 = 97, if you <u>incorrectly</u> took away 50 from 97 and wrote the missing number 47, you can see that $\boxed{47}$ – 50 doesn't equal 97!
Diagonals			
2	B no yes C yes yes D no no E yes no	4	Shape E is a trapezium as it has one set of parallel lines. This particular shape has equal diagonals. Note that not all trapeziums have equal diagonals. For example, this trapezium has unequal diagonals.
Fractions			
3a	$\dfrac{3}{10}$	1	The stick is divided into ten equal parts (the number on the bottom of your fraction) and the cane is as long as 3 parts (the number on the top).
3b	$\dfrac{3}{5}$	1	This question specifies giving your answer in its simplest form. Cane B is as long as six-tenths. $\dfrac{6}{10} = \dfrac{3}{5}$ To simplify fractions, cancel the top and bottom numbers by the same number, in this case by 2.
3c	80%	1	Eight-tenths as a percentage is 80%. If you think of the whole stick as 100%, each part is one-tenth (10%) so eight parts are 80%.
3d	40 cm	1	$\frac{2}{5}$ is the same value as four-tenths. Four-tenths of a metre is 40 cm.
3e	300 cm or 3 m	1	Ten pieces of Cane A measuring 30 cm each would measure 300 cm or 3 m.
3f	Cane E is longer than Cane B but shorter than Cane C.	1	$\frac{2}{3}$ of a metre is 66.6 cm. Cane B is 60 cm and Cane C is 80 cm.

Question number	Answer	Mark	Comments and tips
Money			
4a	£102 or £102.00	1	Note that amounts should never be written with both the **£** sign and a **p** sign, for example £102.00p is wrong.
4b	£1000	1	
4c	£29.70	1	
4d	£15.51	1	To check an answer like this paper, try adding the amount Ged spends to the answer you have written. It should come to £20.
4e	£11.81	1	
Probability			
5a	$\frac{1}{12}$	1	There are 12 coins. The probability of picking the 1p coin is one out of twelve.
5b		1	The probability of picking a 10p coin is four out of twelve. This is the same as one-third or two-sixths.
5c		1	There are 12 coins. The probability of picking a 5p coin is $\frac{2}{12}$ so the probability of not getting a 5p is $\frac{10}{12}$. Note that $\frac{10}{12}$ is the same as $\frac{5}{6}$.
5d		1	The probability of picking a silver coin is $\frac{11}{12}$ as only the 1p is not silver.
5e	Your explanation should include the idea that tests are not always reliable. Davina only tried it 30 times. The probability of picking a 5p is still $\frac{2}{12}$ and the probability of picking a 10p is $\frac{4}{12}$.	1	The greater the number of tests carried out, the more likely the results will match the theoretical probability.
Using letters			
6a	$n + 4$	1	
6b	$n \div 2$ or $\frac{1}{2}n$ or $\frac{n}{2}$	1	Any of these three expressions is acceptable, but the second two are preferable.

Question number	Answer	Mark	Comments and tips
6c	$2n$	1	The answers $n \times 2$ or $2 \times n$ are acceptable, but it is better to shorten the expression to $2n$.
6d	$20n$	1	The answers $n \times 20$ or $20 \times n$ are acceptable, but it is better to shorten the expression to $20n$.
6e	The fish tanks do not hold the same amount. Your explanation should show that $3(n-3)$ becomes $3n-9$ when the brackets are removed.	1	When removing brackets you must multiply whatever is outside the brackets by <u>everything</u> inside the brackets. People sometimes forget and only multiply the first number in the brackets. $3(n-3)$ does NOT equal $3n-3$, but $3n-\mathbf{9}$.
Sequences			
7a	15 21 49 100 1 mark for each correct row.	2	The number of coloured triangles is always 1 more than the shape number doubled. The number of white triangles is always the shape number squared.
7b	$2n+1$ (or equivalent expression) n^2 or $n \times n$ 1 mark for each correct row.	2	The number of coloured triangles is always 1 more than the shape number (n) doubled = $2n+1$. The number of white triangles is always the shape number squared: n^2.
7c	$n^2 + 2n + 1$	1	
7d	Set 2	1	A tip for finding the correct set in a question of this type is to look at the number multiplied by n, in this case 2. Look for the set of shapes which grows by 2 each time.
Angles			
8	$a = 20°$ $b = 65°$ $c = 95°$	3	Angle c is found by subtracting 85° from 180° (angles on a straight line). Angle b is the same as the angle at D (65°), since AB and DE are parallel (these are known as alternate angles, which form a Z shape). The angles inside a triangle add up to 180°. Angle a is found by subtracting b and c from 180°.
Linear equations			
9a	$x = 5$	1	Lines with the equation y = 'a number' are horizontal. Lines with the equation x = 'a number' are vertical. Lines with an equation with x and y are diagonal.

Question number	Answer	Mark	Comments and tips
9b	$y = 2x + 4$	1	In the general equation $y = mx + c$, m stands for the gradient. For this line, the gradient (slope) is the same as for the line AB which is given as 2. The c stands for the y coordinate of the point at which the line would cross the y axis. The line AB crosses at $y = 0$; the line you are finding, DE, crosses at $y = 4$.
9c	$y = 2x + 9$	1	
Areas			
10a	2 cm	2	Remember to look at the formula sheet at the beginning of the test to help you with questions of this type. 1 mark given for using the equation area = $\frac{(a + b)}{2} \times h$ even if answer is incorrect. The area of the parallelogram is 4.5 cm² so the area of the trapezium is therefore 13.5 cm². $13.5 = \frac{(4 + 9.5)}{2} \times h$ $13.5 = \frac{13.5}{2} \times h$ Here you can see that if 13.5 divided by 2 and multiplied by h is 13.5, h must be 2.
10b	Area = $12y^2$	1	Area = $\frac{(2y + 6y)}{2} \times 3y$ $= \frac{8y}{2} \times 3y \quad = 4y \times 3y \quad = 12y^2$

Maths Test 2 Answers

Paper 2

Question number	Answer	Mark	Comments and tips
Running rates			
1a	26 40 14 40 58 18	2	Score 1 mark for each row. Each interval on the vertical axis is worth 2 m.
1b	Your explanation should include the fact that Dev runs at a fairly steady rate, whereas Ben starts more slowly and speeds up, but slows down again near the end.	2	
1c	Ben	1	You can see on the graph that Ben has reached the 60 m line at 8 s.
Square sequences			
2a	Your explanation should show that you have noticed that the two central coloured squares in each shape are represented by $+2$ and the $3n$ represents the three 'legs' on each shape.	1	Notice that the number of coloured squares remains constant and the number of white squares grows. The parts that grow are represented in the expression by a number $\times n$. The constant squares, such as the coloured ones, are represented by just a number.
2b	36 and 2	2	The rule is $3n + 2$. For shape 12, $n = 12$ so $3n + 2 = (3 \times 12) + 2 = 36$ and 2.
2c	20	1	The rule is $3n + 2$. If $3n + 2 = 62$, then $3n = 62 - 2 = 60$. If $3n = 60$, then n must be 20.
2d	$4n + 1$	1	There is 1 central coloured square ($+1$) and 4 'legs' ($4n$), so the total number is $4n + 1$. The equations $1 + 4n$ or $(4 \times n) + 1$ are also acceptable.
Cubes			
3a	A cuboid accurately drawn, e.g. with 3 coloured cubes positioned.	2	The cube can be drawn in a different orientation. Only 1 mark if coloured cubes are not correctly shaded.

86

Question number	Answer	Mark	Comments and tips
3b	2 cm, 2 cm, 2 cm	1	
3c	48 cm³	2	The volume of a cuboid is found by multiplying the length by the width by the height: $3 \times 4 \times 4 = 48$ cm³.
3d	4	1	
3e	$\frac{44}{48}$ or $\frac{22}{24}$ or $\frac{11}{12}$	1	If four cannot be seen then 44 (48 minus 4) can be seen. 44 out of a total of 48 is written as a fraction as $\frac{44}{48}$.
Equations			
4	$x = 3.7$ cm	4	This requires a 'trial and error method'. The result should be checked by putting the value of x into the equation.
Ratio			
5a	480 g	1	The ratio is 4 parts butter for every 3 parts flour. We can write this as the ratio $4:3$. If there is 360 g of flour (one hundred and twenty times the number in the ratio) then butter must be one hundred and twenty times the other number in the ratio, that is $4 \times 120 = 480$.
5b	120 g	1	The ratio is $4:3$. If there is 160 g of butter (forty times the number in the ratio) then flour must be forty times the other number in the ratio, that is $3 \times 40 = 120$.
5c	1500 g flour and 2000 g butter 1 mark each	2	In the ratio $4:3$, there is a total of 7 parts. If a total of 3500 g is mixed (500 times the ratio total) then both butter and flour must be 500 times their numbers in the ratio.
Construction			
6a	To check your answer, measure the perpendicular height of your triangle. If the height is exactly 3 cm then you score 2 marks. If the height is between 2.8 cm and 3.2 cm, you score 1 mark.	2	
6b	22°–24°	1	
Area and circumference			
7a	452.16 cm² or 452 cm² Only 1 mark for the answer 452.389 cm² (use of π button on calculator).	2	Area of a circle $= \pi r^2$. The radius is half the diameter $(24 \div 2) = 12$ Area $= 144 \times \pi = 144 \times 3.14$ NOTE: *If you have used the π button on your calculator your answer will be different. The question stated that π should be taken as 3.14.*

Maths Test 2 Answers – Paper 2

Question number	Answer	Mark	Comments and tips
7b	14 cm	2	The circumference of a circle is $2\pi r$ or πd. If the circumference is 88, then divide 88 by π to find the diameter and then halve to find r.
Sports results			
8a	110	1	Add together 2, 19, 38, 32, 14 and 5.
8b	This graph does not give enough information about the precise distances the students threw.	1	Within the distance 20–29 m, all the students could have thrown over 25 m, in which case Serena is wrong, or under 25 m, in which case she is right.
8c	Again, we need more information.	1	The range of a set of data is found by subtracting the lowest value from the highest value.
8d	29.2 m 1 mark for 29.227 m or 29.23 m.	2	The total values for fx should be divided by 110 (the number of students) to find the mean value.
Heights			
9	False True True False 1 mark for each	4	Since you are told that $b - c = 40$ then Brian must be taller than Caz by 40 cm. We know that Caz is 140 cm, so Brian must be 180 cm. $b + c = a + d$ so $a + d$ must equal $180 + 140 = 320$. Since $a = 165$, then $320 - 165 = 155$ (Darren's height) so he is shorter than Anne.
Field			
10	18 m 3 marks if your working shows the number 44.822 or 45 but the answer is wrong, or if your answer has more than 2 digits, e.g. 18.178. Score 2 marks for the number 2009 in your working.	4	Let x be the length of the path. Use Pythagoras' Theorem ($a^2 + b^2 = c^2$). $35^2 + 28^2 = x^2$ so $x^2 = 2009$, therefore $x = 44.822$ m. Once the distance across the field has been found, add the distances 35 m and 28 m to get 63 m. This value is how far they walked. The difference between 63 m and 44.822 m is 18.178 m, which is 18 m to 2 significant figures.

One mark per correct answer.

1. $\frac{1}{3}$
2. 25
3. 35 000
4. 2500 g
5. $\frac{2}{3}$
6. 32.8
7. 2.5
8. 24%
9. 90 cm^2
10. 20
11. any two numbers with a difference of 8.62, for example 8.63 and 0.01
12. any fraction equivalent to six-sevenths e.g. $\frac{12}{14}$ or $\frac{60}{70}$
13. 27 cm
14. 45
15. 8
16. 1.42
17. 24
18. any value larger than -1 and smaller than 1, for example 0, -0.3, $\frac{1}{2}$
19. 5 and 9
20. about 8
21. $\frac{5}{16}$
22. any three odd numbers that add to 33, for example 25, 5 and 3
23. 51.2
24. $4n$
25. £7.45
26. 9
27. $8^2 - 20$
28. 6 m
29. 4
30. $y - 2 = z + 2$

National Curriculum Levels

Maths Test 2

Write your scores below.

Mark scored in Paper 1   [   ]   out of 45

Mark scored in Paper 2   [   ]   out of 45

Mark scored in Mental Maths Test   [   ]   out of 30

Total score   [   ]   out of 120

Use this table to find the level at which you might be working.

Mark	0–16	17–32	33–65	66–100	101–110	111–120
Level	3	4	5	6	7	8

English at Key Stage 3

Optional tests are designed to help teachers raise standards by providing some extra evidence to support their own assessment. They can:

- help to identify a student's strengths and weaknesses
- help to provide extra support where needed – a case of 'assessment for learning'.

Optional tests at Key Stage 3 are designed for pupils working across Levels 3 to 7 of the National Curriculum for English. There are separate reading and writing tests, plus two Shakespeare papers (on each of two set plays) for Year 9.

Optional tests can be used during key stage 3 to:

- provide valuable diagnostic information about a student's strengths and weaknesses
- be used as summative tests to produce a National Curriculum level.

Please note that teachers may choose to administer the tests alongside written work, class discussions and group activities and that tests are marked internally and results are not collected or published.

About the tests in this book

There are two sets of practice papers in this book. They replicate the optional tests, i.e. you will find:

- English reading test stimulus materials – a variety of written passages on a theme and questions on those texts
- English writing test prompts – some issues to write about and help to structure ideas
- Shakespeare papers for *As You Like It* and *Romeo and Juliet*.

No dictionaries, spell-checkers or thesauri are allowed in the optional tests for English.

Test	Times	Content and marks	NC Levels assessed
Reading	75 minutes, including 15 minutes' reading time	Based upon three texts (32 marks)	Levels 4–7
Writing	75 minutes, including 15 minutes' planning time	Longer Writing Test (30 marks) Shorter Writing Test (20 marks)	Levels 4–7
Shakespeare	45 minutes	Reading and Understanding (18 marks)	Levels 4–7

English at Key Stage 3

The Reading Test

- This paper will include three texts. These will range across genre and can be literary, non-literary, fiction and non-fiction.
- They will be linked according to theme.
- The Reading Test lasts 60 minutes.
- Pupils will be given 15 minutes' reading time on top of this.
- There will be about 15 questions which are varied in format.
- These will take into account pupils' different learning styles.
- Not all questions are of equal difficulty, but the mark scheme will be obvious. There are 32 marks available.

The Writing Test

Writing ability is assessed using two written tests linked to the theme of the Reading Test.

1. A longer test (an open-ended piece). Pupils should spend a longer time on this question. It is worth 30 marks.
2. A shorter test (a more specific and succinct piece). Pupils should not write too much for this question. It is worth 20 marks.

The Writing Test lasts 60 minutes.

Pupils will be given 15 minutes' planning time on top of this.

Pupils will be required to complete both tests. The tests will focus on:

- different purposes;
- different forms of writing.

Planning formats will be provided in both cases.

Information is given about audience and purpose, and usually about the form and the level of formality required in the writing.

They will be marked according to three sets of criteria:

- sentence structure and punctuation;
- text structure and organisation;
- composition and effect.

The Shakespeare Test

The Shakespeare Test for Reading and Understanding will last 45 minutes. It is worth 18 marks. One question only will be set on each play. The question will test understanding of character, themes, language and dramatic conventions. The answer will be assessed only for understanding of the play and for how pupils respond to its literary merits. The test will concentrate on the detailed study of two sections of one of two designated Shakespeare plays for the year. The passages will be printed on the exam paper. For 2013 the designated plays are:

As You Like It
Romeo and Juliet

The set sections for the Year 9 optional English tests are:

- *As You Like It*: **Act 1 Scene 1** (lines 1–55) and **Act 2 Scene 3** (lines 1–68)
- *Romeo and Juliet*: **Act 3 Scene 2** (lines 28–95) and **Act 3 Scene 5** (lines 59–122)

There are two sections specified for each play and students should study both of the set sections.

Each paper (one for each of the two plays) contains a task based on two extracts drawn from one of the set sections. Each paper is based on one of the following four areas of assessment:

- text in performance
- character and motivation
- language of the text
- ideas, themes and issues.

Assessment focuses

Reading assessment focuses
Among the most important are:

- describe, select and retrieve information;
- deduce, infer and interpret information;
- comment on organisation and structure (including grammar and presentation);
- comment on a writer's use of language (including literary features at word and sentence level);
- comment on a writer's purpose and attitude and their effect on the reader;
- relate texts to contexts, e.g. historical or cultural, as well as literary traditions.

Writing assessment focuses
Among the most important are:

- write imaginative, interesting texts;
- write appropriately to topic, audience and purpose;
- organise and structure texts appropriately;
- write and construct coherent paragraphs;
- write clear and varied sentences for effect;
- write with technical accuracy, using appropriate grammar and punctuation;
- select appropriate vocabulary;
- spell words correctly.

Criteria for marking the writing tasks
- sentence structure and punctuation
- text structure and organisation
- composition and effect.

Tips for pupils

- Look at the entire test paper first to establish what has to be done. Highlight the time restraints and the number of questions which need to be answered.
- Which question is worth most marks? Spend more time on that question – but not too much more time. Write the times you need to spend on the questions by the side of them on the question paper.
- Keep an eye on the time! Look at how long you have to spend on a section. When you are practising questions, spend a little longer at first, but aim to become quicker. Remember: you will not be given any extra time in the real test! When you hear 'put your pen down' – that's it!
- Read the questions carefully. Underline key words, e.g. 'compare', 'two reasons …'. Be relevant in your answers.

- Avoid getting too involved with any one question. You may have a great deal to say about it, but it will only be worth a set number of marks.
- Look at how many marks are allocated. Try to make that number of points. If there are 8 marks – make 8 points (and back them up with proof). It won't be that easy really, but it will keep you looking for information and writing until the end.
- Follow the help given on the paper. If the examiners have given a list of points to follow, then use these as the plan for your work. Don't ignore the help you are given on the paper. The examiners tell you what to think about. Use these prompts as a plan for your own reading and writing.
- Make notes on the test paper. Underline important points, circle or highlight information relevant to the question. Underline the key points – or highlight them in some way, or do what is best for you. You can write on the exam papers and it is helpful to do so. You have 15 minutes' reading time to start – no writing then – but you can start to get ideas and remember where key points are to be found. When you go back to underline things you will also be reading the text again. The aim is not to fill in as many sheets in your answer book as possible. You only get the one chance so think about what you want to write before you put your pen to paper.
- Use quotations – but not huge chunks! You are using quotations to back up your points, not to fill up the answer booklet. It is best to quote short phrases and single words.
- If you get stuck on a question, leave it for the moment – but remember to leave a page empty in your answer book in case you want to go back.
- Your basic English is important – you need to communicate what you know and understand. Look carefully for those words you always spell incorrectly! Write in sentences and paragraphs – even leave a line between them – it makes your work easier to read. One rule should always be: make life easy for the examiners!
- If you have time left, go back over your answers.

Advice for parents

Tests and exams can be very stressful. This is mostly because people do not like to feel 'judged' by others – especially if they feel that the results may not be as good as others expect!

The tests in this book are modelled as closely as possible on the 'real thing' so pupils will not be surprised by the test format. However, parents can help with the pressure of the tests by using the material in this book as a resource for teaching and learning. Do not just sit your child down with the test and tell him or her to 'get on with it'; share the experiences, questions and discussion that arise from the tests. Try sitting one yourself!

- Talk about each of the questions and possible ways forward. At this stage, discussion will be more useful than 'writing'.
- Choose a comfortable secure environment in which to do the tests together.
- Mark the work together, praising positive points as well as pointing out things which are not correct.
- Look closely at how the incorrect responses can be corrected, what needs to be learned or changed and how this can be done realistically. It is useful to list just two or three things which need to be done or learned before the next test session.
- Stick to the time limits – but do not insist that the entire test paper has to be completed at one go.
- Give immediate feedback – do not wait too long to discuss your child's performance.
- Be positive about achievements!
- Help your child to formulate specific questions for the teacher about any areas of difficulty.

How important are punctuation and grammar?

Punctuation and grammar are not assessed separately – there is not a fixed mark allocation for how an examiner feels you perform with these two key skills, although they are incorporated into the mark schemes. They are seen as integral to the communication of the ideas in the writing. You can know your subject perfectly, but if you cannot communicate what you know and understand clearly and effectively, then you are not showing yourself at your best. If you look at the criteria for marking on pages 117 and 135, you will find a useful checklist to help you assess your written work. You will be given good marks if your good use of correct spelling and punctuation helps make your meaning clear; conversely, you can expect a less than favourable reaction if inaccuracy stops your reader understanding your work.

Test results

Pages 117–122 and 135–142 show how the marks for this test are correlated. However, the performance on any test in the book is only a guide. They do not guarantee the same result from the real thing! Remember: practice, practice and more practice! No one is motivated by being told they have 'failed'. Use the experience gained from this book to go on to improve performance.

English Test 1

Reading Test

- The paper is 1 hour 15 minutes long.

- You have 15 minutes to read the texts before answering the questions. During this time you should not start to write the answers.

- You then have 1 hour to write your answers.

- Answer all the questions.

- There are 15 questions totalling 32 marks on this paper.

- Check your work carefully.

TIPS

Don't be afraid to underline or circle or highlight the key points in the texts as you are reading them. You can write in the margin of the booklet, too.

95

The theme linking these three passages is 'fireworks'.

Passage 1

*This passage comes from **Plot Night** and describes a celebration on 5th November.*

The bonfire grew smaller, and its heat grew larger. People had to go further and further away from it. It was like a small sun flaming in the night.

John found Daddy and asked him whether he had brought the big rocket. Daddy said he was keeping it to end the show with. He was wondering what to stand it in. Small rockets could be stood in bottles, but this one was so big that it would pull a bottle over. If it did that it would streak across the ground, and might even get out into the road and attack a bus.

Catherine wheels were the best favourite. They had a bad habit of coming off the pin, but when they worked they lasted longest and changed colour all the time. They had come with a little stick, with a pin all ready in the end of it, so that you could hold it. Amy held one, with her eyes tight closed and her face turned away. After that she even came and asked for a banger to be thrown at her. She stood about a yard away, and jumped into the air when it blew up, and ran back to Mother feeling she was the bravest person there…

Mary got by herself, and exploded her fireworks one by one until they were all gone. Then she picked up the bodies and threw them in the fire. One of them was still alive, and spat back a red blob, then a green blob before wrinkling itself up black in the embers.

Andy shared out his fireworks with Nick's gang, who had used theirs up in the last few days. Now they were hungry for them. They took great care to ask Andy to watch his own bangers being lit and his own rockets being sent into space.

The big rocket had to wait until they were all on the way home. There was nothing to stand it in near the bonfire. The only place in the park was the hollow gatepost beside the lane. It was just right. People had filled it half full of stones and gravel, dropping a piece in now and then over the years to see what happened. Now it was just the right depth to hold the bottom of the stick and leave the part that had to be lit over the side.

John helped Daddy stand the rocket in the right place, so that it would go over the park and not over the houses. Then Daddy touched a flame to the blue paper, and it began to glow.

The little red glow took a long time to work. Then it spat once. It glowed more, coughed out some smoke, and then a long tail of flame. The rocket seemed to stand on the flame for a long time, it wasn't really a long time, but just long enough for you to think it hadn't gone yet. Then there was a roar, and the rocket had gone. Before it went it had got itself ready, like a runner, and when it did go it was out to break the record. It looked as if it would never stop. It went up in a curve of fire, then thudded softly, and there was nothing to be seen. Then there was a shower of new bright stars in the sky, dropping, dropping, with smoke above them, and fading as they came. Then each one went out, as if it had gone behind something. In the silence that followed, there was a tumbling sound, and the shell of the rocket, and its stick, rattled in the branches of a tree in the park.

William Mayne

Passage 2

The poem is about how the events of the Guy Fawkes celebrations bring back memories to the poet.

Gunpowder Plot

For days these curious cardboard buds have lain
In brightly coloured boxes. Soon the night
Will come. We pray there'll be no sullen[1] rain
To make these magic orchids flame less bright.

Now in the garden's darkness they begin
To flower: the frenzied whizz of Catherine wheel
Put forth its fiery petals and the thin
Rocket soars to burst upon the steel

Bulwark[2] of a cloud. And then the guy,
Absurdly human phoenix,[3] is again
Gulped by greedy flames: the harvest sky
Is flecked with threshed and glittering golden grain.

'Uncle! A cannon! Watch me as I light it!'
The women helter-skelter, squealing high,
Retreat; the paper fuse is quickly lit,
A cat-like hiss, and spit of fire, a sly

Falter, and then the air is shocked with blast.
The cannon bangs and in my nostrils drifts
A bitter scent that brings the lurking past
Lurching to my side. The present shifts,

Allows a ten-year-old memory to walk
Unhindered now; and so I'm forced to hear
The banshee[4] howl of mortar and the talk
Of men who died, am forced to taste my fear.

I listen for a moment to the guns,
The torn earth's grunts, recalling how I prayed.
The past retreats. I hear a corpse's sons –
'Who's scared of bangers!' 'Uncle! John's afraid!'

Vernon Scannell

[1] miserable or gloomy
[2] a solid wall-like structure built for defence
[3] a mythical creature which died in fire but rose again in the ashes
[4] a frightening ghost

Passage 3

This text is from a fire safety website: www.westsussex.gov.uk

BE SAFE WITH YOUR FIREWORKS

Lucky miss.

FIREWORKS
ARE EXPLOSIVES
FOOLING WITH THEM
CAN MESS YOU UP

Never play with fireworks, they are explosives and can hurt you.

Safety with fireworks

- Only adults should light or hold fireworks.
- When you are watching fireworks, stand well back.
- Never go near a firework that has been lit.
- If you are given a sparkler, **always wear gloves and hold it at arm's length.**
- When your sparkler goes out, **DON'T TOUCH IT**, it could still burn you.
- Put the hot end down in a bucket of water.
- Never give sparklers to a child under five.
- Remember you have to be 18 years old to buy fireworks.

Safety with bonfires

If you are having a bonfire.

- Make sure that the fire is away from fences, garden sheds and properties.
- Never let your children near the fire and cordon off the area.
- Never light the fire using flammable liquids.
- Consider wind direction.
- Keep a bucket of water or a garden hose handy.
- Never leave a bonfire unattended.
- Make sure there are no aerosol cans that may explode.
- Make sure the fire is extinguished before going back indoors.
- Try to go to an organised display in your area.
- Consider nearby properties that may have thatched roofs.

Above all, have a safe and happy night.

Questions 1–5 are about *Plot Night*

1 Find and copy two pieces of information from the first three paragraphs that tell us that we are at a celebration for 5th November. (2 marks)
Focus: Describe, select and retrieve information and events or ideas from the text. Use quotation and reference from the text.

2 Select and copy two pieces of evidence which show that Catherine wheels were Amy's favourite. Explain why you have chosen each piece of evidence. (3 marks)
Focus: Describe, select and retrieve information and events or ideas from the text. Use quotation and reference from the text.

3 Explain the simile in: *It was like a small sun flaming in the night.*
Comment on how effective you think this is as an image for a fire. (2 marks)
Focus: Comment on the writer's use of language, grammatical and literary features (word and sentence level).

4 Place these statements about the final rocket in the correct order. Write the appropriate letter in the correct box below. (2 marks)

- **A** It curved and exploded before disappearing.
- **B** The children heard the used rocket dropping in the park.
- **C** Once lit, it glowed and made some noise but did not seem to move.
- **D** The lights went out and there was silence.
- **E** It made a loud noise and went up into the sky.
- **F** Then it exploded again into a shower of bright lights which streamed downwards.

1	2	3	4	5	6

Focus: Comment on the structure and organisation of texts, grammatical and presentational features (text level).

5 What would make you think that this passage is taken from a book meant for younger children?

You could write about:
- the use of certain types of sentences;
- the length of the sentences;
- the names of the characters;
- the tone of the passage.

(3 marks)
Focus: Comment on the writer's purposes and viewpoints and the effect of the text on the reader.

Questions 6–10 are about *Gunpowder Plot*

6 Quote the evidence from the poem which tells you the location and time of day. (1 mark)
Focus: Describe, select and retrieve information and events or ideas from the text. Use quotation and reference to the text.

7 What image is created of the guy as an 'absurdly human phoenix'? (2 marks)
Focus: Comment on the writer's use of language, grammatical and literary features (word and sentence level).

8 Explain how the fireworks re-create an earlier memory. (2 marks)
   Focus: Deduce, infer and interpret information and events or ideas from the text.

9 The poet uses a particular kind of imagery to describe the fireworks:

   cardboard buds …
   magic orchids …
   they begin/To flower …
   fiery petals …

   Explain the comparisons and comment on how well you think they work in his description of
   the firework party. (2 marks)
   **Focus: Comment on the writer's use of language, grammatical and literary
   features (word and sentence level).**

10 How does the poet build up a picture of the fireworks party in the garden? (5 marks)
    You should comment on:

    ● how he describes the fireworks as they explode;
    ● how he describes the night and the garden;
    ● the reaction of the people to the fireworks;
    ● any sense he appeals to in his imagery;
    ● the comparisons he uses to create pictures and atmosphere.

    **Focus: Identify and comment on the writer's purposes and viewpoints and the
    effect of the text on the reader.**

Questions 11–15 are about *the firework safety website*

11 Quote two words or expressions which tell you that there are two intended audiences for
    this piece of writing. (1 mark)
    **Focus: Describe, select and retrieve information and events or ideas from the
    text. Use quotation and reference to the text.**

12 Explain why some parts of the text are in a larger typeface, in bold or in italics. Give
    examples. (1 mark)
    Focus: Deduce, infer and interpret information and events or ideas from the text.

13 Explain why, when having a bonfire, you should consider:
    wind direction
    nearby properties that may have thatched roofs. (2 marks)
    Focus: Deduce, infer and interpret information and events or ideas from the text.

14 Look at the graphics used and their captions:
    lucky miss
    fireworks are explosives. Fooling with them can mess you up.
    Explain how the writer is playing with language here to get over a difficult message.
    (2 marks)
    **Focus: Comment on the writer's use of language, grammatical and literary
    features (word and sentence level).**

15 Point out the characteristics of this piece that mark it as a set of instructions. (2 marks)
    **Focus: Identify and comment on the writer's purposes and viewpoints and the
    effect of the text on the reader.**

These two writing assignments are linked to the theme of 'fireworks'.

The longer test

- You should spend about 45 minutes on this.
- There are 30 marks available.

> **Write an article for a newspaper to be read in another country, which explains how young people celebrate Guy Fawkes Day on 5th November. Include a description of a typical bonfire party, featuring as much detail as you can.**
>
> In your answer you should:
>
> - use the appropriate style for a piece of journalism;
> - use as much descriptive detail as possible;
> - remember that your audience will not have heard of or understand the significance of this festival.

Planning

Before you start writing, use the format on this page to help you to write notes. Allow time to read your work and check your use of language before you finish.

Planning format

Headline	Introduction Who? What? Where? When? Why? How?
The article itself The details	**Use some experts to quote or to report**
Features of style Past tense Action verbs to create interest Don't use 'I' Subheadings	**Think about your audience** How much will they know? What will have to be explained? How will you appeal to the age group?

The shorter test

- You should spend 30 minutes on this.
- There are 20 marks available.

> **Many people think fireworks should be banned. Write a speech either opposing or defending this point of view to be given to your class.**
>
> - You should write only four paragraphs to explain your point of view, give your evidence and argue your case.
> - Remember to use the appropriate style for a speech – and try to persuade.

Planning

Before you start writing, use the format on this page to help you to write notes. Allow time to read your work and check your use of language before you finish.

Planning format

How will you open your speech?	First paragraph: a direct statement of how you feel and why
Second paragraph: seeing the other point of view	Third paragraph: the evidence for your point of view
Fourth paragraph: the effects of what you propose	How will you close your speech?

Preparing for the Shakespeare Test

There's only one way to prepare for answering questions on a Shakespeare play – read the play! Watching the video is not good enough!

In your test, you will be asked to deal with one aspect of the play you have studied in relation to one or two scenes, but you must also be prepared to share your knowledge of the rest of the play by putting certain aspects of the play into context and saying what has happened before – and if anything has changed – and even what will happen later in the play.

Remember: do not write everything you know about the play – you are not being tested on how good your memory is – and answer the question you have been set, not the one you would have wanted to be set!

Draft your answer before you finally write it.

- Take time to think about what information you need from the scenes printed for you.
- Spend at least 15 minutes reading the scenes carefully.
- Do not be afraid to underline or circle important quotations. Write notes in the margin as you go along.

- Use the helpful pointers given to you on the question paper and write notes on each section. Prove each of your points with a brief quotation.
- Take each of these pointers in turn and think about how to join them together as paragraphs later on. You could even number them in your notes – just to ensure that you do not miss out any.
- Do not write out huge sections from the play. The examiner wants to know what and how you write – not how Shakespeare did!

It is important that you time yourself effectively. You need to pace yourself. You have time to read and annotate the scene printed for you and time to draft and write your answer. You will not be given extra time.

You are being assessed in this section on your knowledge and awareness of the Shakespeare play you have studied – its plot, ideas, the characters and why they behave in the way that they do, the language and even the staging of the scene. But remember, you will also have to write clearly to communicate these ideas. Hence marks are allocated for use of appropriate style, clarity and organisation of writing, spelling, grammar and punctuation, so leave enough time to check your work. Your handwriting is also important.

Reading and Understanding

You should spend about 45 minutes on this section.

Act I Scene I
Act 2 Scene 3

If you were acting in a performance of these scenes from 'As You Like It', what would you have to ensure the audience knew and understood about the characters and themes so that they could appreciate the rest of the play?

Support your ideas by referring to the extracts that are printed on the following pages.

Before you write, you should base your answer on:

- What the characters say.
- What the characters do.
- What others do to them.
- What happens on the stage.
- What impression you want the audience to have.

Read the task again before you begin to write your answer.

Maximum mark: 18

EXAMINER'S TIPS

Remind yourself about the following points:

- Set the scenes in the context of the rest of the play.
- The play begins by setting up a conflict between two brothers that will eventually lead to Orlando fighting with the wrestler Charles and being seen by Rosalind who falls in love with him.
- The danger he faces from his vengeful brother after the match means that he will also have to seek exile in the Forest of Arden.
- There the romance between the lovers can develop.

Many other characters are also seeking exile there and the Forest of Arden will heal them (in the way of pastoral literature), teach them lessons so that they can be reconciled.

Planning sheet

- Use this planning sheet to help you to collect material from the scenes and comment upon it.

Characters	What they say or do	What I learn about them
Oliver		
Orlando		
Adam		

Themes	Explanation	Why they are important to the play
Conflict between brothers		
Gentleness – what it is to be a gentleman		
The pastoral – city life versus country living		

As You Like It

Act 1 Scene 1

Orchard of Oliver's house.

Enter ORLANDO and ADAM

ORLANDO   As I remember, Adam, it was upon this fashion bequeathed me by will but poor a thousand crowns, and, as thou sayest, charged my brother, on his blessing, to breed me well: and there begins my sadness. My brother Jaques he keeps at school, and report speaks goldenly of his profit: for my part, he keeps me rustically at home, or, to speak more properly, stays me here at home unkept; for call you that keeping for a gentleman of my birth, that differs not from the stalling of an ox? His horses are bred better; for, besides that they are fair with their feeding, they are taught their manage, and to that end riders dearly hired: but I, his brother, gain nothing under him but growth; for the which his animals on his dunghills are as much bound to him as I. Besides this nothing that he so plentifully gives me, the something that nature gave me his countenance seems to take from me: he lets me feed with his hinds, bars me the place of a brother, and, as much as in him lies, mines my gentility with my education. This is it, Adam, that grieves me; and the spirit of my father, which I think is within me, begins to mutiny against this servitude: I will no longer endure it, though yet I know no wise remedy how to avoid it.

ADAM   Yonder comes my master, your brother.

ORLANDO   Go apart, Adam, and thou shalt hear how he will shake me up.

Enter OLIVER

OLIVER   Now, sir! what make you here?

ORLANDO   Nothing: I am not taught to make anything.

OLIVER   What mar you then, sir?

ORLANDO   Marry, sir, I am helping you to mar that which God made, a poor unworthy brother of yours, with idleness.

OLIVER   Marry, sir, be better employed, and be naught awhile.

ORLANDO   Shall I keep your hogs and eat husks with them? What prodigal portion have I spent, that I should come to such penury?

OLIVER	Know you where you are, sir?
ORLANDO	O, sir, very well; here in your orchard.
OLIVER	Know you before whom, sir?
ORLANDO	Ay, better than him I am before knows me. I know you are my eldest brother; and, in the gentle condition of blood, you should so know me. The courtesy of nations allows you my better, in that you are the first-born; but the same tradition takes not away my blood, were there twenty brothers betwixt us: I have as much of my father in me as you; albeit, I confess, your coming before me is nearer to his reverence.
OLIVER	*(threatening him)* What, boy!
ORLANDO	*(seizing him by the throat)* Come, come, elder brother, you are too young in this.
OLIVER	Wilt thou lay hands on me, villain?
ORLANDO	I am no villain; I am the youngest son of Sir Rowland de Boys; he was my father, and he is thrice a villain that says such a father begot villains. Wert thou not my brother, I would not take this hand from thy throat till this other had pulled out thy tongue for saying so: thou hast railed on thyself.

Act 2 Scene 3

Before Oliver's house.

Enter ORLANDO and ADAM, meeting

ORLANDO	Who's there?
ADAM	What, my young master? O, my gentle master! O my sweet master! O you memory Of old Sir Rowland! Why, what make you here? Why are you virtuous? Why do people love you? And wherefore are you gentle, strong and valiant? Why would you be so fond to overcome The bonny prizer of the humorous duke? Your praise is come too swiftly home before you. Know you not, master, to some kind of men Their graces serve them but as enemies? No more do yours: your virtues, gentle master, Are sanctified and holy traitors to you. O, what a world is this, when what is comely Envenoms him that bears it!
ORLANDO	Why, what's the matter?
ADAM	O unhappy youth! Come not within these doors; within this roof The enemy of all your graces lives: Your brother – no, no brother; yet the son – Yet not the son, I will not call him son Of him I was about to call his father – Hath heard your praises, and this night he means To burn the lodging where you use to lie And you within it: if he fail of that, He will have other means to cut you off. I overheard him and his practices. This is no place; this house is but a butchery: Abhor it, fear it, do not enter it.
ORLANDO	Why, whither, Adam, wouldst thou have me go?
ADAM	No matter whither, so you come not here.
ORLANDO	What, wouldst thou have me go and beg my food? Or with a base and boisterous sword enforce A thievish living on the common road? This I must do, or know not what to do: Yet this I will not do, do how I can; I rather will subject me to the malice Of a diverted blood and bloody brother.

ADAM   But do not so. I have five hundred crowns,
            The thrifty hire I saved under your father,
            Which I did store to be my foster-nurse
            When service should in my old limbs lie lame
            And unregarded age in corners thrown:
            Take that, and He that doth the ravens feed,
            Yea, providently caters for the sparrow,
            Be comfort to my age! Here is the gold;
            And all this I give you. Let me be your servant:
            Though I look old, yet I am strong and lusty;
            For in my youth I never did apply
            Hot and rebellious liquors in my blood,
            Nor did not with unbashful forehead woo
            The means of weakness and debility;
            Therefore my age is as a lusty winter,
            Frosty, but kindly: let me go with you;
            I'll do the service of a younger man
            In all your business and necessities.

ORLANDO   O good old man, how well in thee appears
            The constant service of the antique world,
            When service sweat for duty, not for meed!
            Thou art not for the fashion of these times,
            Where none will sweat but for promotion,
            And having that, do choke their service up
            Even with the having: it is not so with thee.
            But, poor old man, thou prunest a rotten tree,
            That cannot so much as a blossom yield
            In lieu of all thy pains and husbandry
            But come thy ways; well go along together,
            And ere we have thy youthful wages spent,
            We'll light upon some settled low content.

Shakespeare Test

Romeo and Juliet

Reading and Understanding

You should spend about 45 minutes on this section.

Act 3 Scene 2
Act 3 Scene 5

Imagine that you are directing these scenes. How will you bring out the impact of Tybalt's death on the characters and the plot?

Support your ideas by referring to the extracts that are printed on the following pages.

Before you write, you should base your answer on:

- What the characters say.
- What the characters do.
- What others do to them.
- What happens on the stage.
- What impression you want the audience to have.

Read the task again before you begin to write your answer.

Maximum mark: 18

EXAMINER'S TIPS

Remind yourself about the following points.

- Set the scenes in the context of the rest of the play – the feud between the families; how the lovers meet; the problem they cause; how Romeo gets into the fight with Tybalt; how Tybalt dies and how this leads to Romeo and Juliet planning to escape; what finally happens and why.
- Consider the plot issues: the killing is to start the events which will lead to the tragedy in the end. Tybalt's death keeps up the tension in the play as well as driving the plot.
- The stresses related to what will happen because of the killing will develop Juliet's character and make her seem no longer an innocent girl but very 'grown up'.
- Shakespeare is using irony – the audience knows something but characters on stage do not and this leads to the audience becoming more interested.
- The death also highlights themes such as appearance and reality.

Planning sheet

- Use this planning sheet to help you to collect material from the scenes and comment upon it.

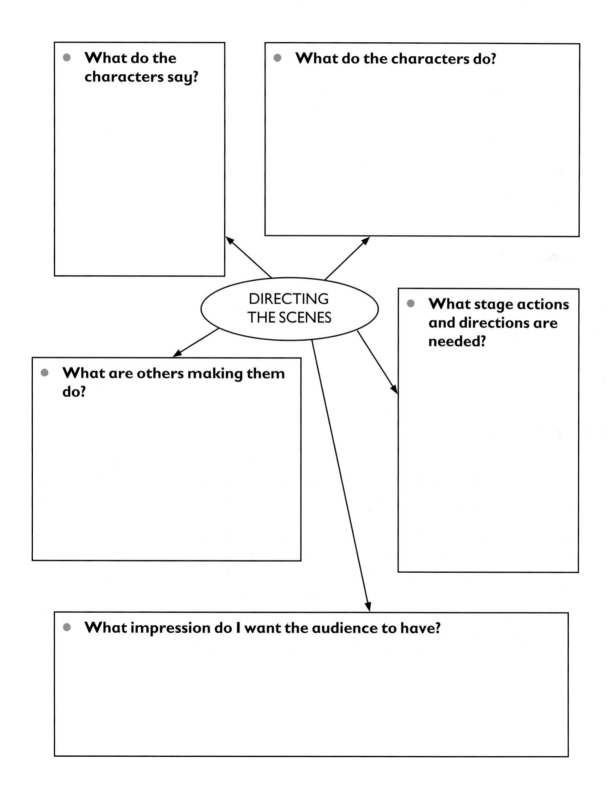

What do the characters say?

What do the characters do?

DIRECTING THE SCENES

What stage actions and directions are needed?

What are others making them do?

What impression do I want the audience to have?

Romeo and Juliet

Act 3 Scene 2

JULIET	O, here comes my nurse,
	And she brings news; and every tongue that speaks
	But Romeo's name speaks heavenly eloquence.
	Enter Nurse, with the ladder of cords
	Now, nurse, what news? What hast thou there? the cords
	That Romeo bid thee fetch?
NURSE	Ay, ay, the cords.
	Throws them down
JULIET	Ay me! what news? why dost thou wring thy hands?
NURSE	Ah, well-a-day! he's dead, he's dead, he's dead!
	We are undone, lady, we are undone!
	Alack the day! he's gone, he's kill'd, he's dead!
JULIET	Can heaven be so envious?
NURSE	Romeo can,
	Though heaven cannot: O Romeo, Romeo!
	Who ever would have thought it? Romeo!
JULIET	What devil art thou, that dost torment me thus?
	This torture should be roared in dismal hell.
	Hath Romeo slain himself? say thou but 'I,'
	And that bare vowel 'I' shall poison more
	Than the death-darting eye of cockatrice:
	I am not I, if there be such an I;
	Or those eyes shut, that make thee answer 'I.'
	If he be slain, say 'I'; or if not, no:
	Brief sounds determine of my weal or woe.
NURSE	I saw the wound, I saw it with mine eyes,
	(God save the mark!), here on his manly breast:
	A piteous corse, a bloody piteous corse;
	Pale, pale as ashes, all bedaub'd in blood,
	All in gore-blood; I swounded at the sight.
JULIET	O, break, my heart! poor bankrupt, break at once!
	To prison, eyes, ne'er look on liberty!
	Vile earth, to earth resign; end motion here;
	And thou and Romeo press one heavy bier!

NURSE	O Tybalt, Tybalt, the best friend I had! O courteous Tybalt! honest gentleman! That ever I should live to see thee dead!
JULIET	What storm is this that blows so contrary? Is Romeo slaughter'd, and is Tybalt dead? My dear-loved cousin, and my dearer lord? Then, dreadful trumpet, sound the general doom! For who is living, if those two are gone?
NURSE	Tybalt is gone, and Romeo banished; Romeo that kill'd him, he is banished.
JULIET	O God! did Romeo's hand shed Tybalt's blood?
NURSE	It did, it did; alas the day, it did!
JULIET	O serpent heart, hid with a flowering face! Did ever dragon keep so fair a cave? Beautiful tyrant! fiend angelical! Dove-feather'd raven! wolvish-ravening lamb! Despised substance of divinest show! Just opposite to what thou justly seem'st, A damned saint, an honourable villain! O nature, what hadst thou to do in hell, When thou didst bower the spirit of a fiend In moral paradise of such sweet flesh? Was ever book containing such vile matter So fairly bound? O that deceit should dwell In such a gorgeous palace!
NURSE	There's no trust, No faith, no honesty in men; all perjured, All forsworn, all naught, all dissemblers. Ah, where's my man? Give me some aqua vitae: These griefs, these woes, these sorrows make me old. Shame come to Romeo!
JULIET	Blister'd be thy tongue For such a wish! he was not born to shame: Upon his brow shame is ashamed to sit; For 'tis a throne where honour may be crown'd Sole monarch of the universal earth. O, what a beast was I to chide at him!
NURSE	Will you speak well of him that kill'd your cousin?

Act 3 Scene 5

JULIET	O fortune, fortune! all men call thee fickle: If thou art fickle, what dost thou with him. That is renown'd for faith? Be fickle, fortune; For then, I hope, thou wilt not keep him long, But send him back.
LADY CAPULET	*[Within]* Ho, daughter! are you up?
JULIET	Who is't that calls? It is my lady mother. Is she not down so late, or up so early? What unaccustomed cause procures her hither?

Enter LADY CAPULET

LADY CAPULET	Why, how now, Juliet!
JULIET	Madam, I am not well.
LADY CAPULET	Evermore weeping for your cousin's death? What, wilt thou wash him from his grave with tears? An if thou couldst, thou couldst not make him live; Therefore, have done: some grief shows much of love; But much of grief shows still some want of wit.
JULIET	Yet let me weep for such a feeling loss.
LADY CAPULET	So shall you feel the loss, but not the friend Which you weep for.
JULIET	Feeling so the loss, Cannot choose but ever weep the friend.
LADY CAPULET	Well, girl, thou weep'st not so much for his death, As that the villain lives which slaughter'd him.
JULIET	What villain madam?
LADY CAPULET	That same villain, Romeo.
JULIET	*[Aside]* Villain and he be many miles asunder, – God Pardon him! I do, with all my heart; And yet no man like he doth grieve my heart.
LADY CAPULET	That is, because the traitor murderer lives.
JULIET	Ay, madam, from the reach of these my hands: Would none but I might venge my cousin's death!

LADY CAPULET	We will have vengeance for it, fear thou not:
	Then weep no more. I'll send to one in Mantua,
	Where that same banish'd runagate doth live,
	Shall give him such an unaccustomed dram,
	That he shall soon keep Tybalt company:
	And then, I hope, thou wilt be satisfied.
JULIET	Indeed, I never shall be satisfied
	With Romeo, till I behold him – dead –
	Is my poor heart for a kinsman vex'd.
	Madam, if you could find out but a man
	To bear a poison, I would temper it;
	That Romeo should, upon receipt thereof,
	Soon sleep in quiet. O, how my heart abhors
	To hear him named, and cannot come to him.
	To wreak the love I bore my cousin
	Upon his body that slaughter'd him!
LADY CAPULET	Find thou the means, and I'll find such a man.
	But now I'll tell thee joyful tidings, girl.
JULIET	And joy comes well in such a needy time:
	What are they, I beseech your ladyship?
LADY CAPULET	Well, well, thou hast a careful father, child;
	One who, to put thee from thy heaviness,
	Hath sorted out a sudden day of joy,
	That thou expects not nor I looked not for.
JULIET	Madam, in happy time, what day is that?
LADY CAPULET	Marry, my child, early next Thursday morn,
	The gallant, young and noble gentleman,
	The County Paris, at Saint Peter's Church,
	Shall happily make thee there a joyful bride.
JULIET	Now, by Saint Peter's Church and Peter too,
	He shall not make me there a joyful bride.
	I wonder at this haste; that I must wed
	Ere he, that should be husband, comes to woo.
	I pray you, tell my lord and father, madam,
	I will not marry yet; and, when I do, I swear,
	It shall be Romeo, whom you know I hate,
	Rather than Paris. These are news indeed!
LADY CAPULET	Here comes your father; tell him so yourself,
	And see how he will take it at your hands.

It is difficult to mark answers in an English test because there is often not a 'right answer' as there could be in Maths. A mark scheme is provided for each question. You will need to judge how well the points made in the answer match with the score criteria. Any point should be clearly stated. Examiners should not have to 'dig' beneath the surface to find the relevant point. The most effective way of assessing work at home is to mark the piece with the candidate so both can see how the final score can be calculated. This will involve discussion of what is in the answer and what has been omitted and so can form a learning experience in itself.

It is also preferable to carry out the task yourself as a parent/carer before marking it. This will make the task clearer and it will also be interesting to see what score you achieve!

Criteria for marking

The Reading Test (marked out of 32)

The marks are allocated for each question on the paper. See pages 118 and 119.

The Longer Writing Test (marked out of 30)

Criteria	Marks possible	NC Level
Sentence structure and punctuation	1–2 3–4 5–6 7 8	Less than 4 4 5 6 7+
Text structure and organisation	1–2 3–4 5–6 7 8	Less than 4 4 5 6 7+
Composition and effect	1–3 4–6 7–9 10–12 13–14	Less than 4 4 5 6 7+

The Shorter Writing Test (marked out of 20)

Criteria	Marks possible	NC Level
Sentence structure, punctuation and text organisation	1–2 3–4 5 6	4 5 6 7+
Composition and effect	1–3 4–6 7–9 10	4 5 6 7+
Spelling	1 2 3 4	4 5 6 7+

The Shakespeare Test (marked out of 18)

Marks are awarded for knowledge of the play, adopting the approach required and use of quotation. See pages 120–121.

English Test 1 Answers
Reading Test

Questions 1–5 are about *Plot Night*

1 'the bonfire grew smaller', 'small rockets could be stood in bottles', 'Catherine wheels were the best favourite' and 'asked for a banger to be thrown at her' are all examples which could be used to achieve the marks. All of these are associated with 5th November celebrations. (2 marks)

2 'best favourite' – the use of two adjectives to make the point of just how good they were. 'she came and asked for a banger to be thrown at her' – she was so excited she became reckless and took part in dangerous activities (not recommended to children). (3 marks)

3 The poet wants to communicate the brightness of the bonfire in the darkness of the night surrounding it. This glowing and burning object is only small so he compares it to 'a small sun', the brightest thing we know, which also gives off heat. It is made even brighter by the comparison of the light and the darkness at night. (2 marks)

4

1	2	3	4	5	6
C	E	A	D	F	B

(2 marks)

5 The subject matter is very exciting to children and the characters in the story are excited by the fireworks. Young children need shorter sentences in texts written for them because they cannot read very well. There are many examples of this. The language and vocabulary are both quite simple. The children call their father 'daddy'. There appears to be a gang at the heart of the story – 'Nick's gang' – and this would appeal to children. The tone of the passage communicates the excitement and explains things carefully and simply. (3 marks)

Questions 6–10 are about *Gunpowder Plot*

6 'Soon the night/Will come' 'in the garden's darkness'. (1 mark)

7 A phoenix is the mythical bird that rises from the ashes. This was a very sophisticated bird. The guy is 'absurdly human' because it looks ridiculous but still looks like a human being. The guy is burned again and again – he is burned every year so he must resurrect himself like the phoenix. The image is faintly ridiculous and sad. (2 marks)

8 The starting point of the bad memory is 'cannon' – a kind of firework but also a gun used in war.
- The imagery changes from that of beauty – flowers, etc. into something more like that expected in war – 'bangs … bitter scent … banshee howl of mortar … torn earth's grunts'.
- All his senses remind him of a time when he fought in the war – ten years ago, 'a ten-year-old memory'. He has a sudden flashback which spoils the party atmosphere. He is afraid, 'taste my fear'.
- The children with him are the children of someone who died in the war, 'a corpse's sons'. The irony is that they as innocent children do not understand why their uncle should be afraid.

(2 marks)

9 *cardboard buds … magic orchids … they begin/To flower … fiery petals …*
These are all images of flowers. The poet describes the fireworks as flowers because they appear to grow as they explode. They are also beautiful colours. The image gives us a sense of the shapes of the fireworks as well. (2 marks)

10
- The poet describes the fireworks as magic 'orchids' which are beautiful, exotic and showy.
- They 'flower' because they are described as 'buds' earlier – they look like something dull curled up or rolled up, but they soon change into something more exciting.
- He continues the imagery with 'fiery petals' – as parts of the firework explode and drop to the earth as petals would fall from a flower. The sparks of the fireworks become 'golden grain' after corn has been threshed.
- They change into weapons – 'rockets … shocked with blast … cannon' and the fire seems sinister – 'greedy flames … spit of fire …'.
- The garden starts as 'dark' and then becomes a 'frenzied' place for a while full of bright light and noise – 'squealing high'.
- People run about in excitement – 'helter-skelter' – and the children with him speak excitedly.
- As well as seeing the fireworks, we can feel the heat, hear the noise, smell the smoke.

(5 marks)

Questions 11–15 are about *the firework safety website*

11 Allow half a mark for recognition of each audience.

children: 'if you are given a sparkler …'; 'remember you have to be 18 …'

adults: 'never let your children …' (1 mark)

12 The design of a page is important to communicate messages – here about safety. Titles are in bold and in larger type to draw attention to them, for example 'Safety with fireworks' so you know where to find the information on the page. Key messages are also made to look different, for example 'always wear gloves …'. Capital letters are used when something needs to be 'shouted' as well, for example 'DON'T TOUCH IT'. (1 mark)

13 Allow one mark for each of the responses.

wind direction: the wind can blow sparks and fire in a specific direction which may be dangerous.

nearby properties that may have thatched roofs: in the country, buildings with thatched roofs can be a fire hazard if a spark blows into them. (2 marks)

14 Allow one mark for each of the responses. Both graphics cleverly use language to communicate the danger of fireworks to young people. They use phrases young people would know and with the visual makes them look at it in a new way.

lucky miss: the phrase is used to describe the young woman in the picture. She has a scar, presumably caused by a firework. It is a small wound so the text is saying that she is lucky. The phrase is not normally associated with people – it normally is used to signify that something has missed its target. Here this could refer to the fact that the firework missed the woman's eye.

fireworks are explosives. Fooling with them can mess you up: 'mess you up' is a slang phrase dealing with emotional turmoil – to 'mess up someone's life'. Here it shows how a firework can 'physically' mess up someone's face by disfiguring them as well as metaphorically 'messing up' someone's life as a consequence of this. (2 marks)

15 Instructions should be written in chronological order and use command verbs and suitable connectives. It also helps if one point is taken at a time as on the website. Bullet points can reinforce the logical order. (2 marks)

As You Like It

Key points – 2 marks for each

1. You will need to make it clear that the play deals with major conflicts between the two pairs of brothers: Oliver and Orlando, and Duke Frederick and Duke Senior. Both end in exile and in the Forest of Arden. Orlando is the younger brother and so did not inherit his father's property, but his rights are being taken from him. Interestingly, in the case of the Duke, it is the *younger* brother who is usurping the rights of the *elder* brother. In Shakespeare's time this would be seen as a sin.

2. In this opening scene, Shakespeare begins to develop a theme common to Elizabethan pastoral literature: "gentleness" or what it means to have those gentlemanly virtues – nobility and a virtuous nature. Elizabethans were interested in whether these qualities could be achieved/learned or whether someone had to be born with them. Orlando seems to be asking this question and 'rustic' characters in the Forest of Arden are there to examine this idea.

3. Orlando's character is introduced to us. He is portrayed to us as someone fairly innocent of the world and in his actions quite inexperienced. This would be because he has not been given the education of a gentleman. When Oliver enters, Orlando has had enough of the situation and decides to fight back. He tells him that "the spirit of my father, which I think is within me, begins to mutiny against this servitude." He is obviously quick to anger and becomes violent with his brother. Orlando grabs Oliver and demands that he receive the education and the treatment due him or else he wants the thousand crowns to which he is entitled to, according to their father's will – but treats his old servant with respect and loyalty – unlike his brother.

4. He is determined, brave and courageous. Shakespeare wants us to see him "grow up" in the forest. Even his own brother says: "he's gentle, never schooled and yet learned, full of noble device, of all sorts enchantingly beloved…" His reaction to his servant and the offer of money shows this.

5. Oliver's own cruel and villainous character is explained in Orlando's opening speech – his father's will has been ignored. Later, Oliver coldly tells Adam, the old and faithful family servant, to leave the room. He lies to Charles, a professional wrestler, and encourages him to harm, if not kill, Orlando. The Duke's wrestler Charles has heard that Orlando intends to come in disguise and "try a fall" with him. Later, Oliver shows his true intent: "I had as lief thou didst break his neck as his finger … I hope I shall see an end of him; for my soul – yet I know not why – hates nothing more than he."

6. The second scene reveals more about Oliver's evil character. When Orlando meets Adam, returning home after the wrestling match, Adam tells him that as he has won, Oliver is plotting to burn down Orlando's sleeping quarters that very night. "Abhor it," Adam warns, "fear it, do not enter it". Oliver will try to murder Orlando by some other means if this does not work. He warns Orlando to leave immediately and offers him his life's savings of five hundred crowns.

7. Adam is very much seen as a "good" character – the epitome of the faithful servant – kind, devoted and thoughtful to the extreme for his master, in contrast with Duke Frederick who may be more educated but is cruel and self-seeking. Orlando also treats him kindly and respects him, even if he is his servant.

8. These conflicts and evil actions between brothers contrast with the idyllic, "pastoral" atmosphere in the Forest of Arden – almost like the world of the fairy tale of Robin Hood, to which we will be introduced soon and where most of the action takes place. Those wounded by life at court are seeking the restorative powers of the country.

9. The scenes also focus on the matter of city life versus country living, a theme throughout the play and something key to Elizabethan thinking. Orlando points out that he is being kept "rustically at home". He is not going away to learn how to be a gentleman. Later, he decides to leave his pastoral home to seek his fortune elsewhere. Later this theme is discussed by Jaques in his famous "All the world's a stage" speech (Act 2, Scene 7) and in the scenes between Touchstone, the fool, and Corin, the country shepherd (Act 3, Scene 2). Much of the debate of the play will be about the corrupt nature of so-called civilised life. People have fled from the forest to escape this and the "natural" people of the forest do not have such sins.

Romeo and Juliet

Key points – 2 marks for each

1. Earlier in the play, Romeo has accidentally killed Tybalt and the Montague–Capulet feud is continued. Romeo is to be banished from Verona – an important plot device. The couple are now secretly married. The killing is to start the events which will lead to the tragedy in the end.

2. In the first scene Juliet longs for the night to come so she can spend the planned night with him. She is unaware of the murderous events of the day and the fact that Romeo has just killed Tybalt – Shakespeare likes to use irony – the audience knows what has happened but the characters on stage do not. So Tybalt's death keeps up the tension in the play as well as driving the plot. As a director you will need to ensure that Juliet is innocent of the crime and her argument with the nurse is convincing.

3. Juliet passes through a variety of moods in the scene as a young girl in love. The stresses related to what will happen now will develop her character and make her seem very "grown up". She is passionate and dreamy to start with in the speech where she imagines him as "little stars", then she becomes concerned thinking him dead and then worried about the impact of Tybalt's death on their plans and happiness. She curses the nurse and praises her lover: "he was not born to shame". As a director you will have to make sure these mood changes are convincing.

4. The nurse does not tell Juliet immediately that she is mistaken – it is as if she is trying to persuade her that Romeo is all that others say he is, but Juliet will not believe this. She does doubt him to begin with : "O serpent heart, hid with a flowering face … beautiful tyrant … fiend angelical." Juliet's love for Romeo is so strong that she would rather kill herself than have to marry Paris, and thus, betray Romeo and their marriage together. This notion of what Juliet is willing to do for love comes up again, as it did before, when she says "I'll no longer be a Capulet." Even though Romeo has killed one of her relatives Juliet keeps faith with him.

5. Juliet is brave enough to go along with the Friar's plan. She is a young, innocent girl but must also be seen as intelligent beyond her years. The friar gives Juliet a sleeping potion that will make it look as if she is dead. She knows that this will be a difficult plan to carry out, but she looks to her love for Romeo to give her the strength to follow it through.

6. The theme of appearance and reality is important in the play – is Romeo both an angel and a devil? The couple need to keep pretending that they are not in love and married. In the end their attempt to appear dead will lead to both of their deaths – a tragedy – but this will also bring the two families together. Characters on stage will not know what has happened even though the audience does. This needs to be carefully managed by a director.

7. Lady Capulet mistakes Juliet's tears for Romeo as grief for Tybalt's death – again ironic for the audience and something linked to the appearance and reality theme. Juliet even threatens vengeance, promising to have Romeo poisoned in Mantua. Juliet is becoming cleverer in what she is doing to be with her lover, but fate will mean that they both die. Juliet shows considerable courage to defy her parents and go to Friar Laurence.

8. In the second scene, Juliet and the fugitive Romeo part after having spent the night together. The scene shows something of how Juliet has grown up and her relationship with her mother and the nurse. The change in character from innocent young girl to thoughtful adult needs to be shown by the character on stage and the actors.

9. Lady Capulet tells her that she must marry Paris on Thursday and Juliet refuses – she, and the audience, know why. It is because of this that the whole plot to do with poison via Friar Laurence develops and leads to both their deaths, and the tragedy.

National Curriculum Levels

English Test 1

The following are National Curriculum Writing criteria for Levels 4 and 6. Judge work by how many of the features are included and how effectively. Imagine a line marked off in Levels 4 to 7. Where does the answer fit on that line according to the criteria below?

Level 4	Level 6
The pupils' ideas are generally clear. There is some attempt to organise them into a suitable form. Pupils are beginning to choose words effectively. There is some use of grammatically correct sentences. Punctuation to mark sentences is mostly used accurately and pupils are beginning to use punctuation within the sentence. Spelling of simple and common longer words is generally accurate. Handwriting is mostly clear and legible.	The pupils' writing is interesting in parts, using suitable style for the task. The quality of the writing is enhanced by a varied vocabulary, a range of simple and complex sentences and appropriate paragraphing. A range of punctuation is usually used correctly to clarify meaning. Spelling is usually accurate. Handwriting is in a fluent and legible form.

The English Tests taken together are worth a total of 100 marks. Use the following table to find at which overall level you might be working.

Score	Criteria	NC Level
93–100	Exceptional answers	Level 7+
75–92	Well above average answers	Level 7
56–74	Above average answers	Level 6
40–55	Average or below average answers	Level 5
20–39	Well below average answers	Level 4 or below

- The paper is 1 hour 15 minutes long.
- You have 15 minutes to read the texts before answering the questions. During this time you should not start to write the answers.
- You then have 1 hour to write your answers.
- Answer all the questions.
- There are 15 questions totalling 32 marks on this paper.
- Check your work carefully.

> **TIPS**
>
> Don't be afraid to underline or circle or highlight the key points in the texts as you are reading them. You can write in the margin of the booklet, too.

The theme linking these three passages is 'perceptions of old age'.

Passage 1

This passage comes from 'Great Expectations' by Charles Dickens and tells of Pip's first sight of Miss Havisham when he was a child.

In an arm-chair, with an elbow resting on the table and her head leaning on that hand, sat the strangest lady I have ever seen, or shall ever see.

She was dressed in rich materials – satins and lace, and silks – all of white. Her shoes were white. And she had a long white veil dependent* from her hair, and she had bridal flowers in her hair, but her hair was white. Some bright jewels sparkled on her neck and on her hands, and some other jewels lay sparking on the table. Dresses, less splendid than the dress she wore, and half-packed trunks, were scattered about. She had not quite finished dressing, for she had but one shoe on – the other was on the table near her hand – her veil was but half arranged, her watch and chain were not put on, and some lace for her bosom lay with those trinkets, and with her handkerchief and gloves, and some flowers, and a Prayer-Book, all confusedly heaped about the looking glass.

It was not in the first few moments that I saw all these things, though I saw more of them in the first moments than might be supposed. But, I saw that everything within my view which ought to be white, had been white long ago, and had lost its lustre, and was faded and yellow. I saw that the bride within the bridal dress had withered like the dress, and like the flowers, and had no brightness left but the brightness of her sunken eyes. I saw that the dress had been put upon the rounded figure of a young woman, and that the figure upon which it now hung loose, had shrunk to skin and bone. Once I had been taken to see some ghastly waxwork at the Fair, representing I know not what impossible personage lying in state. Once I had been taken to one of our old marsh churches to see a skeleton in the ashes of a rich dress, that had been dug out of a vault under the church pavement. Now, waxwork and skeleton seemed to have dark eyes that moved and looked at me. I should have cried out, if I could.

* dependent = hanging

'Who is it?' said the lady at the table.

'Pip, ma'am.'

'Pip?'

'Mr Pumblechook's boy, ma'am. Come – to play.'

'Come nearer; let me look at you. Come close.'

It was when I stood before her, avoiding her eyes, that I took note of the surrounding objects in detail, and saw that her watch had stopped at twenty minutes to nine, and that the clock in the room had stopped at twenty minutes to nine.

'Look at me,' said Miss Havisham. 'You are not afraid of a woman who has never seen the sun since you were born?'

Passage 2

Warning

When I am an old woman I shall wear purple
With a red hat which doesn't go and doesn't suit me,
And I shall spend my pension on brandy and summer gloves
And satin sandals and say we've no money for butter.
I shall sit down on the pavement when I'm tired
And gobble up samples in shops and press alarm bells
And run my stick along the public railings
And make up for the sobriety* of my youth.
I shall go out in my slippers in the rain
And pick the flowers in other people's gardens
And learn to spit.

You can wear terrible shirts and grow more fat
And eat three pounds of sausages at a go
Or only bread and pickle for a week
And hoard pens and pencils and beermats and things in boxes.

But now we must have clothes that keep us dry
And pay our rent and not swear in the street
And set a good example for the children.
We will have friends to dinner and read the papers.
But maybe I ought to practise a little now?
So people who know me are not too shocked and surprised
When suddenly I am old and wear purple.

Jenny Joseph

* sobriety = self-control

Passage 3

This text is an extract from a website.

Did You Know?

Home : Did you know?

Help the Aged is Britain's leading charity working with and for older people.

Our long-term plan is to attack and remove things which stop older people from living happy and successful lives. Our four urgent priorities are:

- Combating poverty
- Reducing loneliness, encouraging community
- Defeating negative ideas about age
- Making sure older people receive good care

We have a vision of a future where older people are valued, have lives that are richer and voices that are heard.

We want to encourage everyone to value older people so that they don't need to feel lonely or afraid, are not treated badly and are treated with dignity and respect, so they can have as much fun as young people.

What we do to help older people in the UK and abroad

Advice and information

- **SeniorLine:** We make sure older people always have someone to talk to on the telephone. Senior Line (0808 800 6565) is an advice line providing information for older people with problems such as benefits and pensions.
- **Information leaflets:** We have over 50 of these which help older people and their families.

Services

- **Transport:** We provide transport so that older people can get out and about. Special vehicles have been given to 1,600 groups, helping to keep them mobile and active.
- **HandyVan:** HandyVan fitters help older people feel safe in their own homes by fitting devices such as door chains, window locks and smoke detectors. Sixty thousand older people's homes have been secured.
- **Gardening:** We provide gardening help for older people because if people's gardens look tidy and cared for their houses are less likely to be burgled.

Fundraising

- **Adopt a Granny:** This is a scheme where people can donate a small amount of money each month to help support and care for an older person living in developing countries.
- **Research:** We do research into how people age to help ensure a healthier future for everyone.

Speaking up for our age

- Older people want to change things and sometimes form groups to make a difference on issues which are important to them. We help to support these groups so that they can make things happen.
- We talk to national, regional and local government about the things that matter to older people.

These are just a few examples of all the work the Charity does. Visit the main Help the Aged site at www.helptheaged.org.uk to find out more.

Questions 1–5 are about the passage from _Great Expectations._

1 Find and quote two examples to show that Miss Havisham was originally preparing for a wedding. (1 mark)
Focus: Describe, select and retrieve information and events or ideas from the text. Use quotation and reference to the text.

2 Point out how Pip's description of Miss Havisham proves his idea that she is 'the strangest lady I have ever seen'. (2 marks)
Focus: Comment on the writer's use of language, grammatical and literary features (word and sentence level).

3 Write what you learn about the character of the old lady and why she is behaving as she is. (2 marks)
Focus: Deduce, infer and interpret information and events or ideas from the text.

4 Comment on the effectiveness of the following: that is, show what the descriptions add to the author's intention in the passage.
Once I had been taken to see some ghastly waxwork at the Fair, representing I know not what impossible personage lying in state. Once I had been taken to one of our old marsh churches to see a skeleton in the ashes of a rich dress, that had been dug out of a vault under the church pavement. Now, waxwork and skeleton seemed to have dark eyes that moved and looked at me. (3 marks)
Focus: Comment on the writer's use of language, grammatical and literary features (word and sentence level).

5 Show how the writer effectively creates the scene from the point of view of a child. (4 marks)
You should write about:
- the tone of the writing;
- how the boy becomes aware of what is happening;
- his reaction to what he sees;
- how he responds to what he sees and is asked;
- the unusual images and description used by the writer.

Focus: Identify and comment on the writer's purposes and viewpoints and the effect of the text on the reader.

Questions 6–10 are about _Warning_

6 Find and quote a phrase from the poem which shows that the author is looking forward to a time when she is old. (1 mark)
Focus: Describe, select and retrieve information and events or ideas from the text. Use quotation and reference to the text.

7 List four things which the poet says she will be able to do when she is old. (2 marks)
Focus: Describe, select and retrieve information, events or ideas from the text. Use quotation and reference to the text.

8 Explain how the poet contrasts what people expect of an old lady with how she would like to behave. (2 marks)

In your answer you should comment on:
- what the poem says in the final section about what is expected;
- how the earlier images contrast with this;
- how the writer feels about this;
- how the reader feels about this.

Focus: Deduce, infer and interpret information and events or ideas from the text.

9 The poet uses the verb 'gobble',

And gobble up samples in shops.

Comment on how well you think the verb works in the characterisation of the woman. (2 marks)

Focus: Comment on the writer's use of language, grammatical and literary features (word and sentence level).

10 The definition of someone who is 'eccentric' is: 'not following the established pattern of conduct; odd'. Explain whether you think the lady in this poem deserves this description. (5 marks)

In your answer you should comment on:

● what you expect the established 'pattern of conduct' might be for a lady such as the one in the poem;

● what she would like to do and why;

● how you feel about this.

Focus: Identify and comment on the writer's purposes and viewpoints and the effect of the text on the reader.

Questions 11–15 are about the *Help the Aged* website

11 Explain the vision of Help the Aged. (1 mark)
Focus: Describe, select and retrieve information and events or ideas from the text.
Use quotation and reference to the text.

12 Find and quote a sentence from the passage which explains why the gardening service for old people is so important. (1 mark)
Focus: Describe, select and retrieve information and events or ideas from the text. Use quotation and reference to the text.

13 Explain in your own words why it is important that the Help the Aged programme encourages 'everyone to value older people'. (2 marks)
Focus: Deduce, infer and interpret information and events or ideas from the text.

14 Explain what the value of the bold headings could be in this kind of writing and what other organisational and design features help to make the explanation clearer. (2 marks)
Focus: Comment on the structure and organisation of texts, grammatical and presentational features (text level).

15 Explain the impact on the meaning of the sentences of the words in bold in the two examples. (2 marks)

We provide transport so that older people can get out and about. **Special** vehicles have been given to 1,600 groups, helping to keep them mobile and active.	HandyVan fitters help older people feel safe in their own homes by fitting devices such as door chains, window locks and smoke detectors. Sixty thousand older people's homes have been **secured**.

Focus: Comment on the writer's use of language, grammatical and literary features (word and sentence level).

These two writing assignments are linked to the theme of 'perceptions of old age'.

The longer test

- You should spend about 45 minutes on this.
- There are 30 marks available.

> **You go to visit an old person in a care home as a part of a class project. Describe this person and the place in which they live and how you feel about them.**
>
> **Use the passage from 'Great Expectations' and the poem 'Warning' to give you some ideas.**
>
> In your answer you should:
>
> - use an appropriate style for a description or piece of imaginary writing
> - concentrate on the person and his or her surroundings to give your reader a sense of these
> - consider how you feel about the situation and why.

Planning

Before you start writing, use the format on this page to help you to write notes. Allow time to read your work and check your use of language before you finish.

Planning format

Introduction: Will you start when you are there already and then fill in detail, or will you start by explaining why you are there?	The place: details
The person: details	**How you react: use your senses. What do you smell, hear, see and feel?**
What do you say?	**Conclusion: What is your lasting impression or what have you learned?**

The shorter test

- You should spend about 30 minutes on this.
- There are 20 marks available.

You are fundraising for the charity 'Help the Aged'. Write the text for a leaflet that will persuade people to give you money in support of your cause.

Use the Help the Aged passage to provide you with information.

In your answer you should:

- use an appropriate style for a piece of persuasive writing
- concentrate on the most important information and use language to show that these are vital services
- consider devices such as subheadings and bullet points that may help you communicate your ideas more effectively for the audience.

Planning

Before you start writing, use the format on this page to help you to write notes. Allow time to read your work and check your use of language before you finish.

Planning format

What are you trying to achieve?	Who is your audience?
What are the most important pieces of information that you need?	**How will you make these seem important to support through giving money?**
Where can you divide your text, using subheadings to pinpoint important information, or using bullet points to summarise to make for easy reading?	**What information will you provide so the funds can be collected? What information will you ask for?**

Reading and Understanding

You should spend about 45 minutes on this section. You can find the full text on pages 106–109.

Act 1 Scene 1
Act 2 Scene 3

You have been asked to summarise the ideas, themes and issues of *As You Like It*, and present them to another class, just by using these two scenes. Write what you would say to them.

Support your ideas by referring to the extracts that are printed on the following pages.

Before you write, you should base your answer on:

- What the characters say.
- What the characters do.
- What others do to them.
- What this says about Shakespeare's intentions.
- What impression Shakespeare wants to give the audience.

Read the task again before you begin to write your answer.

Maximum mark: 18

EXAMINER'S TIPS

Remind yourself about the following points.

- Set the scenes in the context of the rest of the play.
- The play begins by setting up a conflict between two brothers that will eventually lead to Orlando fighting with the wrestler Charles and being seen by Rosalind who falls in love with him.
- The danger he faces from his vengeful brother after the match, means that he will also have to seek exile in the Forest of Arden.
- There the romance between the lovers can develop.
- Many other characters are also seeking exile there and the Forest of Arden will heal them (in the way of pastoral literature) and teach them lessons so that they can be reconciled.

Each of these plot lines is meant to illustrate and develop themes or issues. Make sure that you summarise these.

Planning sheet

- Use this planning sheet to help you to collect material from the scenes and comment upon it. Add further themes or issues to the chart.

Themes and issues in the scenes		
	Explanation and proof from the text	**Why they are important to the play**
Conflict between brothers		
Gentleness – what it is to be a gentleman		
The pastoral – city life versus country living		
Good versus evil, and how this is shown		

Reading and Understanding

You should spend about 45 minutes on this section. You can find the full text on pages 112–115.

Act 3 Scene 2
Act 3 Scene 5

In a tragedy, events have unforeseen consequences. Often these lead to the tragedy developing and ultimately to the deaths of the main characters at the end. How do the events in these scenes lead to 'unforeseen consequences' throughout the play?

Support your ideas by referring to the extracts that are printed on the following pages.

Before you write, you should base your answer on:

- What the characters say.
- What the characters do.
- What others do to them.
- How characters react.

Read the task again before you begin to write your answer.

Maximum mark: 18

EXAMINER'S TIPS

Remind yourself about the following points.

- Set the scenes in the context of the rest of the play – the feud between the families; how the lovers meet; the problem they cause; how Romeo gets into the fight with Tybalt; how Tybalt dies and how this leads to Romeo and Juliet planning to escape; what finally happens and why.
- Consider the plot issues: the killing is to start the events that will lead to the tragedy in the end. Tybalt's death keeps up the tension in the play as well as driving the plot.
- The stresses related to what will happen because of the killing will develop Juliet's character and make her seem no longer an innocent girl but very 'grown up' and so she starts to plan.
- Shakespeare is using irony – the audience knows something but characters on stage do not and this leads to the audience becoming more interested.

Planning sheet

- Use this planning sheet to help you to collect material from the scenes and comment upon it. Add further events to the chart.

Event	Reference from text	Unforeseen consequences
Romeo has accidentally killed Tybalt and the Montague–Capulet feud is continued.		
Romeo is to be banished from Verona.		
The couple are now secretly married.		
Juliet goes along with the Friar's plan.		
Lady Capulet tells her that she must marry Paris on Thursday and Juliet refuses.		

It is difficult to mark answers in an English test because there is often not a 'right answer' as there could be in Maths. A mark scheme is provided for each question. You will need to judge how well the points made in the answer match with the score criteria. Any point should be clearly stated. Examiners should not have to 'dig' beneath the surface to find the relevant point. The most effective way of assessing work at home is to mark the piece with your child so both can see how the final score can be calculated. This will involve discussion of what is in the answer and what has been omitted and so can form a learning experience in itself.

It is also preferable to carry out the task yourself as a parent/carer before marking it. This will make the task clearer and it will also be interesting to see what score you achieve!

Criteria for marking

The Reading Test (marked out of 32)

The marks are allocated for each question on the paper. See pages 136–138.

The Longer Writing Test (marked out of 30)

Criteria	Marks possible	NC Level
Sentence structure and punctuation	1–2 3–4 5–6 7 8	Less than 4 4 5 6 7+
Text structure and organisation	1–2 3–4 5–6 7 8	Less than 4 4 5 6 7+
Composition and effect	1–3 4–6 7–9 10–12 13–14	Less than 4 4 5 6 7+

The Shorter Writing Test (marked out of 20)

Criteria	Marks possible	NC Level
Sentence structure, punctuation and text organisation	1–2 3–4 5 6	4 5 6 7+
Composition and effect	1–3 4–6 7–9 10	4 5 6 7+
Spelling	1 2 3 4	4 5 6 7+

The Shakespeare Test (marked out of 18)

Marks are awarded for knowledge of the play, adopting the approach required and use of quotation. See pages 139–141.

English Test 2 Answers
Reading Test

Questions 1–5 are about the passage from *Great Expectations.*

1   The question asks for quotations, so these must be given to achieve the mark. Choose any
    two of:
    '…satins and lace, and silks – all of white. Her shoes were white. And she had a long white veil…'
    'bridal flowers in her hair'
    'and some flowers, and a Prayer-Book …'
    'I saw that the bride within the bridal dress…'
    (1 mark)

2   The novel is in the form of an autobiography and is narrated from the first person point of
    view – 'I'. Pip is obviously young and has been called to the house. He does not know why
    – 'come to play' – so is nervous. What he sees obviously shocks him, as it is eccentric and
    bizarre – out of his experience.
    She is dressed in old white clothes – obviously wedding clothes.
    The room seems to be in confusion with jewels and clothes scattered all over.
    Miss Havisham is only wearing one shoe.
    She reminds him of a corpse – shrunken and faded – 'skin and bone' … 'a skeleton'.
    The clocks had all been stopped at the same time.
    She has not 'seen the sun' – been out of the room – for many years.
    All these go some way to prove his idea that she is 'the strangest lady I have ever seen'.
    (2 marks)

3   We can only deduce what has happened. Her wedding has been stopped for some reason and
    she has never changed her clothes since. The clocks were stopped at 'twenty minutes to nine'
    so we presume there is a reason for this – this is when her life was considered to stop, and she
    has not been in the outside world since. She ignores the young child to begin with and makes
    no effort to make him feel more at ease. She is then firm with him – 'Look at me'.
    (2 marks)

4   The boy has never seen anything like Miss Havisham before so he reaches back into his
    memory to rationalise what he sees. Dickens gives us images that conjure up Miss Havisham
    as something which is dead and dusty, something that has not seen the light for many years.
    In this way he not only gives us a picture of her but also makes her more scary and builds the
    atmosphere in this eerie room from a child's point of view.

    'some ghastly waxwork at the Fair, representing I know not what impossible personage lying
    in state' is the image of a dead body – shocking for a child. 'a skeleton in the ashes of a rich
    dress, that had been dug out of a vault under the church pavement' is even more visual – in
    this case he sees a real dead body but something whose clothes have rotted and whose skin
    has shrunk over time around the skull. For the child and for the reader, the really scary thing
    is that these images seem to come alive in front of the child: 'Now, waxwork and skeleton
    seemed to have dark eyes that moved and looked at me.'
    (3 marks)

5   The passage starts rationally enough with Pip, the child, simply stating a fact: '…sat the
    strangest lady I have ever seen'. She takes no notice of him – it is almost as if she is a
    'waxwork' – so he continues to inspect and describe her in a cool tone – only what he sees to
    start with. This is the way a child would react. The room is also presumably dark as

Miss Havisham says she has not seen the 'light of the sun' for some time so this must have been even more frightening. He sees parts of things and strange groups of things as he tries to remember this later on. Remember that this uses the 'I' first person narrator so is a form of autobiography. It is all so strange, he cannot see it as real; he sees it almost as a picture. It is only when he starts to think about it that he reaches back into his limited experience to try to find something comparable. It is then that he comes out with the startling images of the skeleton and the waxwork – now come to life like something in a horror film. Only then does he become afraid: 'I should have cried out, if I could'. The impression is that he was so afraid that he was silenced. When he does talk, he is polite and nervous, only stating what he has been told, 'Mr Pumblechook's boy, ma'am. Come – to play.' He avoids her eyes and notices that this is a room where time has stood still.

(4 marks)

Questions 6–10 are about *Warning*

6   'I shall wear purple …' (future tense). 'But maybe I ought to practise a little now?'
   (1 mark)

7   'wear purple …with a red hat which doesn't go … spend my pension on brandy … sit down on the pavement' (there are many more).
   (2 marks)

8   The final section of the poem gives an indication of what society expects, for example clothes are functional – to keep her dry – not to be colourful or shocking. Her money should be spent on practical things such as paying her rent, not on making her life pleasurable in its last stages. The way she speaks is even regulated by society's expectations, for example she is not expected to swear. Old people are expected to set a good example to the 'younger generation' and not act in outrageous ways. However, the younger generation are permitted to do this in some ways. There is a sense that this was not always the case and this old lady seems to have 'missed out' on this. She will 'have friends to dinner'.

All the earlier images – colourful clothes, shocking activities – are seen as in direct contrast to society's 'normal' rules.

The lady is obviously not really old when she is writing the poem as she wants to 'practise' so people will not be too shocked later. There is a sense in which she has made up her mind to do some of these things.
   (2 marks)

9   *And gobble up samples in shops.* The poet could have used a simple verb such as 'eat' but this verb suggests eating greedily and without manners – all the things that she is looking forward to being able to do – to break all of society's expectations of how she should behave.
   (2 marks)

10   The interest in the poem lies in the fact that the narrator can fantasise about what it might be like to offend the conventions of society. We do not know whether she will actually do any of these 'shocking' things, but they appeal to our sense of the absurd. In fact there is no reason why old ladies should not behave in this way – but if they did they would be considered 'eccentric'.

The clothes she suggests are shocking because of their bright colours – our expectation is that old ladies should wear sober colours. She suggests spending her money on luxuries rather than on essentials – even though our expectation is that pensioners are not very 'well off'. Her actions, for example sitting on the pavement, playing with a stick like a child, would be out of character with our expectations of 'the older generation'. Generally, the old lady wants to be an individual – not bound by the rules of society. She wants to make up for the 'sobriety' of her youth. She will even do shocking things – stealing flowers, spitting, eating huge amounts of one thing.

The scene is amusing because of the contrast with our expectations, but there is also a hint of sadness in the poem. She has been restricted all her life by what society says she must do. Even in her old age she has to follow rules – in fact there may be even more rules for older people.

(5 marks)

Questions 11–15 are about the *Help the Aged* website

11 Help the Aged has 'a vision of the future where older people are valued, have lives that are richer and voices that are heard.'
(1 mark)

12 'if people's gardens look tidy and cared for their houses are less likely to be burgled.'
(1 mark)

13 It is important for others to value older people so they become people in their own right. They should not be lonely – people should mix with them – and in doing this they will become less afraid of an often confusing world. They should not be treated badly just because they are old and should have as many rights as younger people.
(2 marks)

14 The bold headings make the ideas much clearer and highlight the important issues. The website has to include much information about the work of Help the Aged and this helps to make it easier to read. Other design features include the use of bullet points to draw our eyes to the points and the first important words in a sentence also being in bold.
(2 marks)

15 'special' makes the vehicles not seem 'ordinary'. They have been specially modified for the needs of the old – they are not just any vehicle and reflect upon the specialist work of Help the Aged. 'Secured' sounds much less aggressive than 'made safe' and is less likely to frighten people.
(2 marks)

Answers should include these key points, illustrated by suitable quotations.

As You Like It

Key points – 2 marks for each

1. You will need to make it clear that the play deals with major conflicts between the two pairs of brothers: Oliver and Orlando, and Duke Frederick and Duke Senior. Both end in exile and in the Forest of Arden. Orlando is the younger brother and so did not inherit his father's property, but his rights are being taken from him. Interestingly, in the case of the Duke, it is the *younger* brother who is usurping the rights of the *elder* brother. In Shakespeare's time this would be seen as a sin.

2. In this opening scene, Shakespeare begins to develop a theme common to Elizabethan pastoral literature: "gentleness" or what it means to have those gentlemanly virtues – nobility and a virtuous nature. Elizabethans were interested in whether these qualities could be achieved/learned or whether someone had to be born with them. Orlando seems to be asking this question and "rustic" characters in the Forest of Arden are there to examine this idea.

3. Orlando's character is introduced to us. He is portrayed to us as someone fairly innocent of the world and in his actions quite inexperienced. This would be because he has not been given the education of a gentleman. When Oliver enters, Orlando has had enough of the situation and decides to fight back. He tells him that "the spirit of my father, which I think is within me, begins to mutiny against this servitude." He is obviously quick to anger and becomes violent with his brother. Orlando grabs Oliver and demands that he receive the education and the treatment due him or else he wants the thousand crowns to which he is entitled to, according to their father's will – but treats his old servant with respect and loyalty – unlike his brother.

4. He is determined, brave and courageous. Shakespeare wants us to see him "grow up" in the forest. Even his own brother says: "he's gentle, never schooled and yet learned, full of noble device, of all sorts enchantingly beloved…" His reaction to his servant and the offer of money shows this.

5. Oliver's own cruel and villainous character is explained in Orlando's opening speech – his father's will has been ignored. Later, Oliver coldly tells Adam, the old and faithful family servant, to leave the room. He lies to Charles, a professional wrestler, and encourages him to harm, if not kill, Orlando. The Duke's wrestler Charles has heard that Orlando intends to come in disguise and "try a fall" with him. Later, Oliver shows his true intent: "I had as lief thou didst break his neck as his finger … I hope I shall see an end of him; for my soul – yet I know not why – hates nothing more than he."

6. The second scene reveals more about Oliver's evil character. When Orlando meets Adam, returning home after the wrestling match, Adam tells him that as he has won, Oliver is plotting to burn down Orlando's sleeping quarters that very night. "Abhor it," Adam warns, "fear it, do not enter it". Oliver will try to murder Orlando by some other means if this does not work. He warns Orlando to leave immediately and offers him his life's savings of five hundred crowns.

7. Adam is very much seen as a "good" character – the epitome of the faithful servant – kind, devoted and thoughtful to the extreme for his master, in contrast with Duke Frederick who may be more educated but is cruel and self-seeking. Orlando also treats him kindly and respects him, even if he is his servant.

8. These conflicts and evil actions between brothers contrast with the idyllic, "pastoral" atmosphere in the Forest of Arden – almost like the world of the fairy tale of Robin Hood, to which we will be introduced soon and where most of the action takes place. Those wounded by life at court are seeking the restorative powers of the country.

9. The scenes also focus on the matter of city life versus country living, a theme throughout the play and something key to Elizabethan thinking. Orlando points out that he is being kept "rustically at home". He is not going away to learn how to be a gentleman. Later, he decides to leave his pastoral home to seek his fortune elsewhere. Later this theme is discussed by Jaques in his famous "All the world's a stage" speech (Act 2, Scene 7) and in the scenes between Touchstone, the fool, and Corin, the country shepherd (Act 3, Scene 2). Much of the debate of the play will be about the corrupt nature of so-called civilised life. People have fled from the forest to escape this and the "natural" people of the forest do not have such sins.

Romeo and Juliet

Key points – 2 marks for each

1. Earlier in the play, Romeo has accidentally killed Tybalt and the Montague–Capulet feud is continued. Romeo is to be banished from Verona – an important plot device for the tragedy to continue because he does not receive his letter later on and returns to find Juliet "dead". The couple are now secretly married. The killing is to start the events which will lead to the tragedy in the end.

2. In the first scene Juliet longs for the night to come so she can spend the planned night with him. She is unaware of the murderous events of the day and the fact that Romeo has just killed Tybalt – Shakespeare likes to use irony – the audience knows what has happened but the characters on stage do not. So Tybalt's death keeps up the tension in the play as well as driving the plot. She can only think about the future with her new love.

3. Juliet passes through a variety of moods in the scene as a young girl in love. She starts to plot the device that will ensure their escape – but this goes wrong. She seeks a help from Friar Laurence. The plan they come up with is that Juliet would consume a drug that would take her into a coma for nearly three hours. Romeo was to be told of the plan via a messenger, who doesn't reach him in time. On the eve of her marriage to Count Paris, Juliet takes the drug and is declared dead.

4. The nurse does not tell Juliet immediately that she is mistaken – it is as if she is trying to persuade her that Romeo is all that others say he is, but Juliet will not believe this. She does doubt him to begin with: "O serpent heart, hid with a flowering face … beautiful tyrant … fiend angelical." Juliet's love for Romeo is so strong that she would rather kill herself than have to marry Paris, and thus, betray Romeo and their marriage together. This notion of what Juliet is willing to do for love comes up again, as it did before, when she says "I'll no longer be a Capulet". Even though Romeo has killed one of her relatives Juliet keeps faith with him.

5. Juliet is brave enough to go along with the Friar's plan. She is a young, innocent girl but must also be seen as intelligent beyond her years. The friar gives Juliet a sleeping potion that will make it look as if she is dead. She knows that this will be a difficult plan to carry out, but she looks to her love for Romeo to give her the strength to follow it through.

6. The theme of appearance and reality is important in the play – is Romeo both an angel and a devil? The couple need to keep pretending that they are not in love and married. In the end their attempt to appear dead will lead to both of their deaths – a tragedy – but this will also bring the two families together. Romeo hears about her "death" and buys poison before visiting the family crypt. In another unintended consequence Paris encounters Romeo and is killed by the latter. Believing that his lady-love is dead, Romeo drinks the poison. When Juliet awakes to discover Romeo's corpse, she stabs herself.

7. Lady Capulet mistakes Juliet's tears for Romeo as grief for Tybalt's death – again ironic for the audience and something linked to the appearance and reality theme. Juliet even threatens vengeance, promising to have Romeo poisoned in Mantua. Juliet is becoming cleverer in what she is doing to be with her lover, but fate will mean that they both die. Juliet shows considerable courage to defy her parents and go to Friar Laurence.

8. In the second scene, Juliet and the fugitive Romeo part after having spent the night together. The scene shows something of how Juliet has grown up and her relationship with her mother and the nurse. The change in character from innocent young girl to thoughtful adult needs to be shown by the character on stage and the actors.

9. Lady Capulet tells her that she must marry Paris on Thursday and Juliet refuses – she, and the audience, know why. It is because of this that the whole plot to do with poison via Friar Laurence develops and leads to both their deaths, and the tragedy.

National Curriculum Levels

English Test 2

The following are National Curriculum Writing criteria for Levels 4 and 6. Judge work by how many of the features are included and how effectively. Imagine a line marked off in Levels 4 to 7. Where does the answer fit on that line according to the criteria below?

Level 4	Level 6
The pupils' ideas are generally clear. There is some attempt to organise them into a suitable form. Pupils are beginning to choose words effectively. There is some use of grammatically correct sentences. Punctuation to mark sentences is mostly used accurately and pupils are beginning to use punctuation within the sentence. Spelling of simple and common longer words is generally accurate. Handwriting is mostly clear and legible.	The pupils' writing is interesting in parts, using suitable style for the task. The quality of the writing is enhanced by a varied vocabulary, a range of simple and complex sentences and appropriate paragraphing. A range of punctuation is usually used correctly to clarify meaning. Spelling is usually accurate. Handwriting is in a fluent and legible form.

The English Tests taken together are worth a total of 100 marks. Use the following table to find at which overall level you might be working.

Score	Criteria	NC Level
93–100	Exceptional answers	Level 7+
75–92	Well above average answers	Level 7
56–74	Above average answers	Level 6
40–55	Average or below average answers	Level 5
20–39	Well below average answers	Level 4 or below

Science at Key Stage 3
Preparing for the tests
You can specifically improve your marks by taking into account the following points:

The language used in the questions

1. The examiners will not put any useless information in a question. If something is written down then the examiner wants you to use it.

   Example *Space probes have shown that there are **mountains, dry river valleys** and **volcanoes** on Mars. Scientists believe Mars, like Earth, has all three types of rock: **igneous, metamorphic** and **sedimentary**.* You will need to use all the terms.

2. Use the mark scheme to tell you how many points you should include in your answers.

3. Read the question very carefully.

   Example *Tick the correct box.* Only tick one box. The mark scheme will probably indicate to the marker that if more than one box has been ticked the question should be marked incorrect.

4. Don't be put off if you encounter unfamiliar material. You will know enough science to answer the question. In the example above you may not know much about Mars. However, the work you have done on rock formation on Earth will let you answer the question.

Key words found in the questions

1. **Choose** from a list of words. Make sure you use words from the list. Unless the paper states otherwise, you can use words more than once. Similarly you don't have to use them all.

2. **Describe...** You do **not** have to explain anything; you simply have to make a physical description of a diagram, graph etc.

   Example If you are asked to describe a graph you might say 'From 1950 to 1967 the number of people suffering from measles varied from year to year but overall remained constant at around 5 per 100 000. From 1967 to 1981 the number of people suffering from measles again varied from year to year but decreased from around 5 per 100 000 to 1 per 100 000.' You do not have to explain **why** it remained constant and then decreased.

3. **Explain...** You need to give a scientific explanation for your answer. Include some key scientific words in your answer.

   Example The plant in flask C receives *light*, which it needs for *photosynthesis*.

4. **Predict...** There are two possible types of prediction:
   - Predicting what you think might happen in an investigation.
   - Extrapolating a graph (continuing a trend) to predict what might happen in the future.

5. Be aware of **negatives**.

   Example *Give the name of another metal, **not** in the table...*

6. **Advantages and disadvantages**. To be on the safe side, make sure you state both things in your comparisons.

   Example *Give **one** advantage of using biomass rather than fossil fuel as an energy resource.* Energy from biomass is renewable whereas energy from fossil fuels is non-renewable.

7. **Name... Which... What... Give...** These are simple command words which require a simple response. These are often found with numbers or words in bold type.

Sitting the practice tests

There are two practice tests in this book. Remember that the practice tests are designed to help you get used to what are sometimes called 'examination conditions'. In other words, when you take the tests you will be given an exact time (60 minutes) and be expected to work in silence with no books or other people to help you. That is exactly how you should practise.

1. You need a pencil or pen and a watch or clock.
2. Make sure that you have somewhere quiet to work.
3. Ask someone to time the test so that you have exactly 60 minutes.
4. If you cannot read a scientific word then someone can read it to you. That person should not tell you what it means.
5. Do not rush at the test as soon as the timer starts. Take a few deep breaths and try to relax.
6. Do not start answering the questions until you have had a look at all of the test paper. This will give you a good idea of what is covered in the test and how many questions there are.
7. Read each question carefully and follow the instructions.
8. Do not spend too long over any one question. Answer it and move on.
9. If you can't answer a question, don't worry. Move on to the next one. You can always come back at the end.
10. Try to use all of the time available. If you think you have finished, go back and check every question. Make sure you have not made silly mistakes or missed a question out.
11. At the end of the time, check your answers with the mark scheme and work out your total.
12. Make a list of the questions you did not do too well on, but congratulate yourself on those you answered well.
13. Discuss the questions you found most difficult with a parent or a teacher. It is a good idea to check your notes to make sure that the topic won't cause problems again.

After a few weeks, try the questions again. You will improve your score if you have been working and revising and you will be well prepared for the real thing.

Refer to pages 166 and 196 to find out what National Curriculum Level you might be working at.

1 The diagram below shows some organisms that live in ponds.

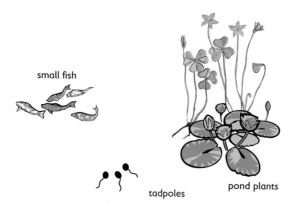

small fish

pond plants

tadpoles

The graph below shows how the populations of the plants, tadpoles and small fish changed over time.

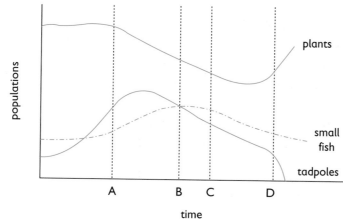

At time A on the graph the tadpoles are hatching from the frog spawn.

a How did this affect the population of the pond plants?

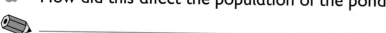

1

b How was the small fish population in the pond affected between times A and B?

1

Explain why this happened.

1

TOTAL

3

1

c Use the information on the graph to explain why the small fish population began to fall at time C.

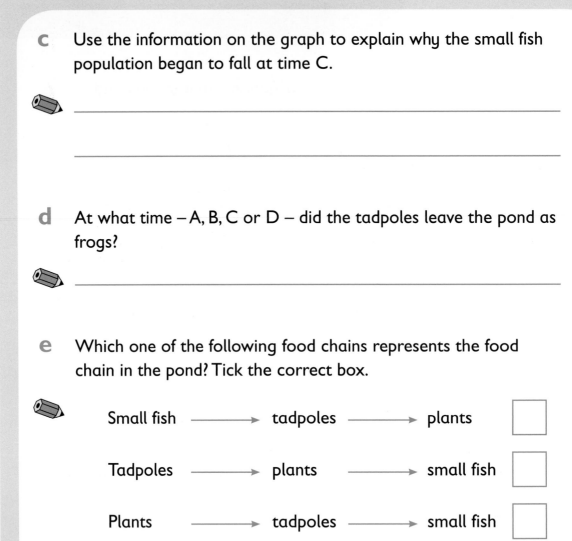

_____

_____

1

d At what time – A, B, C or D – did the tadpoles leave the pond as frogs?

_____

1

e Which one of the following food chains represents the food chain in the pond? Tick the correct box.

Small fish   ⟶   tadpoles   ⟶   plants   ☐

Tadpoles   ⟶   plants   ⟶   small fish   ☐

Plants   ⟶   tadpoles   ⟶   small fish   ☐

TOTAL

3

2 The chart shows one way to group animals with backbones.

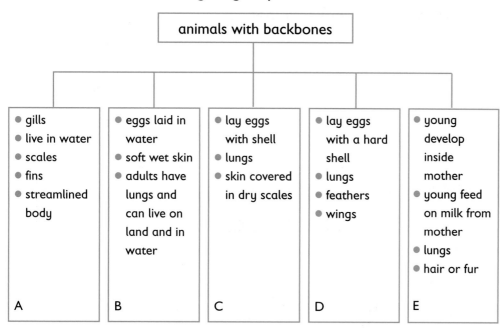

• gills • live in water • scales • fins • streamlined body	• eggs laid in water • soft wet skin • adults have lungs and can live on land and in water	• lay eggs with shell • lungs • skin covered in dry scales	• lay eggs with a hard shell • lungs • feathers • wings	• young develop inside mother • young feed on milk from mother • lungs • hair or fur
A	B	C	D	E

a To which group (A, B, C, D or E) do the following living things belong?
Each letter may be used **once, more than once** or **not at all**.

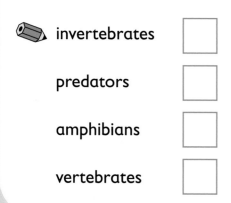

frog _____

goldfish _____

snake _____

gorilla _____

sparrow _____

b What is the name given to animals with a backbone?
Tick the correct box.

invertebrates ☐

predators ☐

amphibians ☐

vertebrates ☐

5

1

TOTAL

6

147

3   The information below was taken from the labels of a loaf of bread and a tin of baked beans.

Nutritional information		
	Baked beans per 100 g	**Bread per 100 g**
Energy	331 kJ	920 kJ
Protein	4.5 g	11.0 g
Total carbohydrate	16.6 g	39.0 g
Sugar	5.5 g	1.0 g
Fat	0.3 g	2.0 g
Fibre	3.5 g	7.0 g
Sodium	0.5 g	0.5 g

a   Which of the two foods, bread or baked beans, has the lower sugar content?

_____

1

b   Which of the two foods provides more energy for exercise?

_____

1

c   Which of the two foods has the higher protein content?

_____

1

d   Give **one** reason why we need protein in our diet.

_____

_____

1

TOTAL

4

4 Magnesium nitrate is formed when magnesium reacts with dilute nitric acid. A gas is also produced.

a What do the following signs mean when found in word equations?

+

_____

→

_____

1

1

b Write a word equation for the chemical reaction producing magnesium nitrate.

[   ] + [   ] ⟶ [   ] + [   ]

2

5 David adds some sugar to his tea.

a Which words in the list below describe the sugar, the tea and the sweet tea? Complete the table.

solvent   solute   filtrate   sediment   solution

3

Substance	Word
tea	
sugar	
sweet tea	

TOTAL

7

149

b David wants to find out how to make the sugar dissolve more quickly. What **two** things could he try?

1. _____

2. _____

2

c Suggest **two** factors that must be kept constant in order to make this investigation a fair test.

1. _____

2. _____

2

d Is unsweetened tea a pure substance or a mixture?
Tick the correct box.

pure substance ☐   mixture ☐

1

Explain your answer.

_____

_____

_____

1

TOTAL

6

6 The diagram below shows a cell of a bacterium.

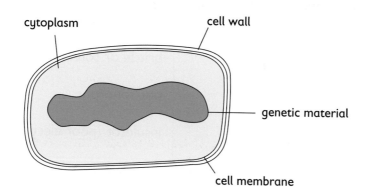

cytoplasm

cell wall

genetic material

cell membrane

a There are some important differences between the cell of a bacterium and a plant cell. Chose which of the following statements are true or false by ticking the correct box.

i The cells of bacteria are larger than plant cells. ☐ True ☐ False

ii The cells of bacteria have no cell wall. ☐ True ☐ False

iii The cells of bacteria are much smaller than plant cells. ☐ True ☐ False

iv The cells of bacteria have no nucleus. ☐ True ☐ False

4

b Bacteria can be useful to us but some also cause diseases.

i How do white blood cells help to protect you from diseases?

_____

_____

1

ii How do your skin cells help to protect you from diseases?

_____

_____

1

TOTAL

6

7a This table gives some of the properties of metals and non-metals.

Metal	Non-metal
malleable and ductile	brittle or soft
sonorous (rings when hit)	not sonorous
good electrical conductor	insulator (poor electrical conductor)
good heat conductor	insulator (poor heat conductor)
surface is shiny	surface is dull
usually high density	low density

From the list of properties give a reason why:

i saucepan handles are often made from plastic

_____

_____

ii some metals are used to make necklaces and earrings

_____

_____

iii plastic, a non-metal, is used to cover electric wires

_____

_____

iv radiators are made from metal

_____

_____

4

TOTAL

4

b Some kitchen spoons are made from plastic and metal – usually stainless steel.

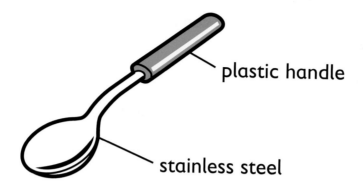

plastic handle

stainless steel

i Give one reason why the handle is made from plastic.

_____

1

ii Give **two** reasons why the spoon is made from stainless steel.

1. _____

2. _____

2

iii Would you select a metal or a non-metal to make the bottom of a saucepan?

_____

1

Explain your answer.

_____

_____

1

TOTAL

5

153

8a A fuel is a substance that is burnt to release energy.

i Name a solid fuel that can be burnt in an open fire to provide heat.

_____

_____

1

ii Name a fuel that is a liquid, stored in tanks and can be burnt in a boiler for central heating systems.

_____

_____

1

iii Name a fuel that is a gas and can be burnt to heat an oven.

_____

_____

1

b Here are some of the energy sources that people use:

tides	oil	wind
coal	sun	natural gas

TOTAL

3

List three of these energy sources that might be in short supply over the next few hundred years.

i _____

1

ii _____

1

iii _____

1

c Electric ovens can be used to cook food. The electrical energy is generated in power stations that burn fossil fuels.

i Give two ways that burning fossil fuels in power stations causes problems in the environment.

_____

_____

2

ii In the electric cooker the electrical energy is transferred into which type of energy?

_____

1

TOTAL

6

9 Tony and Rafa are investigating light and mirrors. A diagram of their apparatus is shown below.

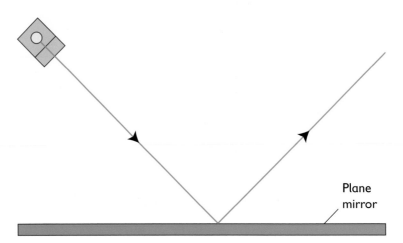

Plane mirror

a Add the following labels to the diagram.

ray box
incident ray
reflected ray

3

b Draw and label the normal line.

1

c Draw and label the angle of incidence.

1

d Draw and label the angle of reflection.

1

TOTAL

6

10 The diagrams show four different types of cells.

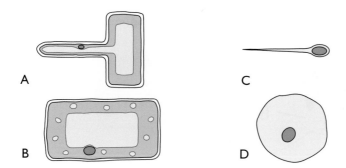

A

C

B

D

a Which two of the cells are animal cells?

Cell [   ] is an animal cell.

Cell [   ] is an animal cell.

2

b Which cell is able to swim to fertilise an egg?

Cell [   ]

1

c Which cell will be able to carry out the process of photosynthesis?

Cell [   ]

1

d Which cell is a plant cell but without chloroplasts?

Cell [   ]

1

e Write down two differences between plant and animal cells.

Difference 1

_____

2

Difference 2

_____

TOTAL

7

157

11 The diagram shows the Earth in orbit around the Sun.

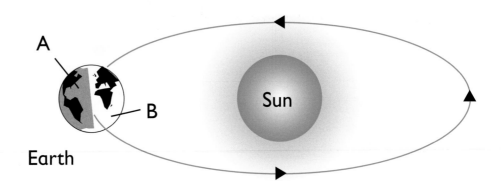

A

Sun

B

Earth

a Give the names of **two** planets in the solar system which are closer to the Sun than the Earth.

1. _____

2. _____

2

b Give the names of **two** planets in the solar system which are further away from the Sun than the Earth.

1. _____

2. _____

2

c The distance a planet is from the Sun affects two things: the temperature of the planet and the length of a year (the time it takes the planet to orbit the Sun).

Tick the correct box.

A planet that is near to the Sun will have:

a high surface temperature and a long year ☐

a low surface temperature and a short year ☐

a high surface temperature and a short year ☐

a low surface temperature and a long year ☐

1

TOTAL

5

d Look at the diagram of the Earth and Sun on the previous page.

i Explain why it is night time at point A.

_____

_____

1

ii Explain why it is day time at point B.

_____

_____

1

iii Will it be day time or night time at A in **12** hours' time?

_____

Explain your answer.

_____

_____

2

e On the diagram, draw the position of the Earth three months later than shown.

Explain why you have drawn the Earth in this position.

_____

_____

2

TOTAL

6

159

12 Michelle has just sprayed perfume onto her neck. After five minutes her friends sitting across the room notice the aroma.

a Explain why her friends could smell the perfume after five minutes.

_____

_____

_____

_____

3

b

Which sentence best describes what is happening to Michelle's perfume?
Tick the correct box.

i The perfume is dissolving in the air. ☐

ii The perfume is diffusing through the air. ☐

iii The perfume is melting. ☐

1

TOTAL

4

c   The box below on the left shows the arrangement of particles in the liquid perfume. In the box on the right, draw the arrangement of the particles five minutes after the perfume is sprayed.

1

d   Which of the statements below is true about the particles in the room after five minutes?
Tick the correct box.

The particles are all perfume molecules. ☐

The particles are perfume liquid and perfume vapour. ☐

The particles are a mixture of air molecules and perfume molecules. ☐

The particles are all air molecules. ☐

1

e   What is the name of the process whereby a gas or vapour spreads out?
Tick the correct box.

freezing ☐   condensation ☐

filtration ☐   diffusion ☐

1

TOTAL

3

13a A piece of coal is an energy resource. How is the energy stored in a piece of coal?
Tick the correct box.

as kinetic energy ☐

as potential energy ☐

as chemical energy ☐

as thermal energy ☐

1

b When coal is burned, energy is transferred from the coal to its surroundings. Complete the boxes below to show the energy change involved.

| ----------------------------- | changes to → | ----------------------------- |

energy in coal   energy

2

TOTAL

3

162

c   In a coal power station there are many stages between burning the coal and generating the electricity. These stages are shown below.

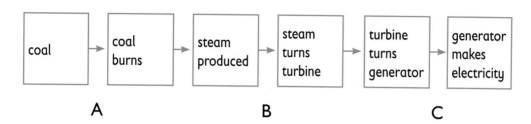

coal → coal burns → steam produced → steam turns turbine → turbine turns generator → generator makes electricity

A   B   C

Each of the stages (A, B and C) involves an energy transfer.

i   Which letter represents the change

thermal energy ⟶ kinetic energy? ☐

1

ii   Which letter represents the change

kinetic energy ⟶ electrical energy? ☐

1

iii   Which letter represents the change

chemical energy ⟶ thermal energy? ☐

1

TOTAL

3

Science Test 1 Answers

Question number	Answer	Mark	Comments and tips
1a	The population declines (goes down).	1	
1b	The population increases. The hatching of the tadpoles provides more food, therefore more fish can survive and reproduce.	2	
1c	As the tadpole population decreases, there is less food to sustain the fish population.	1	
1d	D	1	
1e	Plants → tadpoles → small fish should be ticked.	1	
2a	frog – B goldfish – A snake – C gorilla – E sparrow – D	5	
2b	Vertebrates should be ticked.	1	Vertebrate means having a backbone.
3a	Bread	1	
3b	Bread	1	
3c	Bread	1	
3d	One of the following: for growth, to build muscles, or for repair.	1	
4a	+ means added to and → means gives or produces (accept either).	2	
4b	magnesium + nitric acid → magnesium nitrate + hydrogen	2 (half mark for each)	
5a	tea – solvent sugar – solute sweet tea – solution	3	
5b	Any two from: Use smaller lumps of sugar. Stir the tea. Use hotter water.	2	
5c	Use the same quantity of sugar. Use the same quantity of tea.	2	
5d	It is a mixture. It is a mixture of hot water and substances from the tea leaves.	2	
6a	i. False ii. False iii. True iv. True	4	
6b	i. The white blood cells attack bacteria and destroy them. ii. The skin's cells act as a barrier to stop bacteria entering your body.	1 1	
7a	i. Plastics do not conduct heat (insulator). ii. Metal is shiny or metal is malleable or ductile.	4	

Question number	Answer	Mark	Comments and tips
	iii. Plastics do not conduct electricity (insulator). iv. Metals conduct heat.		
7b	i. Plastic is a heat insulator. ii. Any two from: The steel is malleable (can be shaped). The steel is shiny. The steel is hard (has a high density). iii. A metal, because it will conduct heat from the hob.	1 2 2	
8a	i. coal ii. oil iii. natural gas (methane)	1 1 1	
8b	i. coal ii. oil iii. natural gas	1 1 1	
8c	i. Accept producing smoke or sulphur dioxide (acid gases) and producing carbon dioxide to increase green house gases/global warming. ii. Thermal (heat)	2 1	
9a	Label pointing to ray box, incident ray (left-hand ray) and reflected ray (right-hand ray)	3	
9b	Normal line added at 90° to the mirror where the incident and reflected rays meet.	1	
9c	The angle made between the normal line and incident ray is labelled.	1	
9d	The angle made between the normal line and reflected ray is labelled.	1	
10a	C and D are animal cells.	2	
10b	Cell C	1	
10c	Cell B	1	
10d	Cell A	1	
10e	Cell wall, vacuole; chloroplasts	2	
11a	Mercury and Venus	2	
11b	Any two from: Mars, Jupiter, Saturn, Uranus, Neptune	2	
11c	A high surface temperature and a short year.	1	
11d	i. A is facing away from the Sun. ii. B is facing towards the Sun. iii. Day time. The Earth will have turned half-way round and so will face the other way.	1 1 2	
11e	The Earth should be drawn directly below the Sun on the diagram. It will have travelled one quarter of its yearly orbit in 3 months.	2	The Earth takes one year to orbit the Sun completely.
12a	The perfume liquid evaporates (1 mark) and the particles spread into the room (1 mark). The particles take time to spread or diffuse across the room (1 mark).	3	

Question number	Answer	Mark	Comments and tips
12b	The perfume is diffusing through the air.	1	
12c	The diagram should show that the particles are widely spaced.	1	
12d	The particles are a mixture of air molecules and perfume molecules.	1	
12e	diffusion	1	
13a	as chemical energy	1	
13b	chemical thermal *or* heat	2	
13c	i. B ii. C iii. A	1 1 1	

National Curriculum Levels

Science Test 1

Maximum marks: 90

Mark	0–33	34–46	47–59	60–75	76–90
Level	Below 4	4	5	6	7

1 The information in the table shows the recommended daily amounts of nutrients and energy for different people.

Person	Energy	Protein	Iron	Calcium
Farm worker	12 000 kJ	60 g	10 mg	650 mg
Office worker	10 000 kJ	58 g	10 mg	650 mg
15-year-old boy	11 000 kJ	54 g	11 mg	950 mg
15-year-old girl	8 000 kJ	44 g	15 mg	800 mg
(approximate values)				

a Give one reason why the office worker needs a lower-energy diet than the farm worker.

_____

_____

1

b Iron is needed to make red blood cells. Explain why 15-year-old girls need more iron than 15-year-old boys.

_____

_____

1

c Give one reason why 15-year-old boys and girls need more calcium than adults.

_____

_____

1

TOTAL

3

d i Which of the following foods would be the best source of calcium for the 15-year-olds?
Tick one box.

1

celery ☐   margarine ☐

milk ☐   chicken ☐

ii Which of the foods would be the best source of protein?
Tick one box.

1

celery ☐   margarine ☐

milk ☐   chicken ☐

iii Which of the foods would be the best source of fibre?
Tick one box.

1

celery ☐   margarine ☐

milk ☐   chicken ☐

TOTAL

3

2   The diagram shows an important organ system in females.

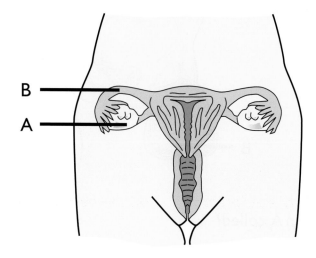

a   What is the name of this organ system?

_____

1

b   Eggs are produced in organ A. What is the name of organ A?

_____

1

c   The eggs travel down tube B. What is the name of tube B?

_____

1

TOTAL

3

The diagram below shows the equivalent organ system in males.

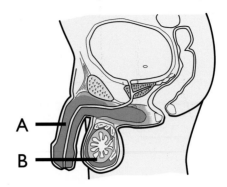

d What is organ A called?

 _____

1

e Sperm cells are made in organ B. What is organ B called?

 _____

1

f Use the words below to complete the description.

6

| placenta | fertilised | embryo | divides | uterus | sperm |

When _____ cells meet an egg cell one of them may enter.

The egg cell is _____. The egg cell then travels to the

_____ where it becomes embedded in the thick wall. The

egg cell _____ and develops into an _____. This

is given food from the mother via the _____.

TOTAL

8

3a The diagram below shows human lungs.

   i   Write the names of A, B and C.

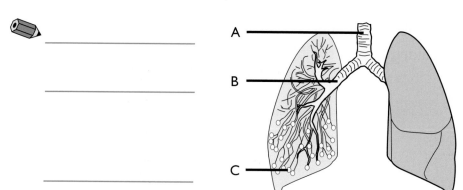

_____

_____

_____

3

   ii   In each lung there are many branches. Each branch ends at the part labelled C.
Explain how this arrangement helps humans to breathe more effectively.

_____

_____

1

   iii   Part A has rings of material called cartilage. Suggest **one** reason why these rings of cartilage are present.

_____

_____

1

b   The diagram shows an example of part C in more detail.

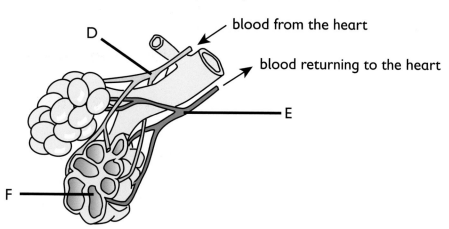

blood from the heart

blood returning to the heart

D

E

F

i   Give one reason why part F has such a rich blood supply.

1

_____

ii Describe **two** differences between the blood flowing in capillary D and the blood flowing in capillary E.

2

1. _____

2. _____

c   Stewart was being tested for asthma. He was asked to breathe into a machine to test how much air he could breathe into and out of his lungs.

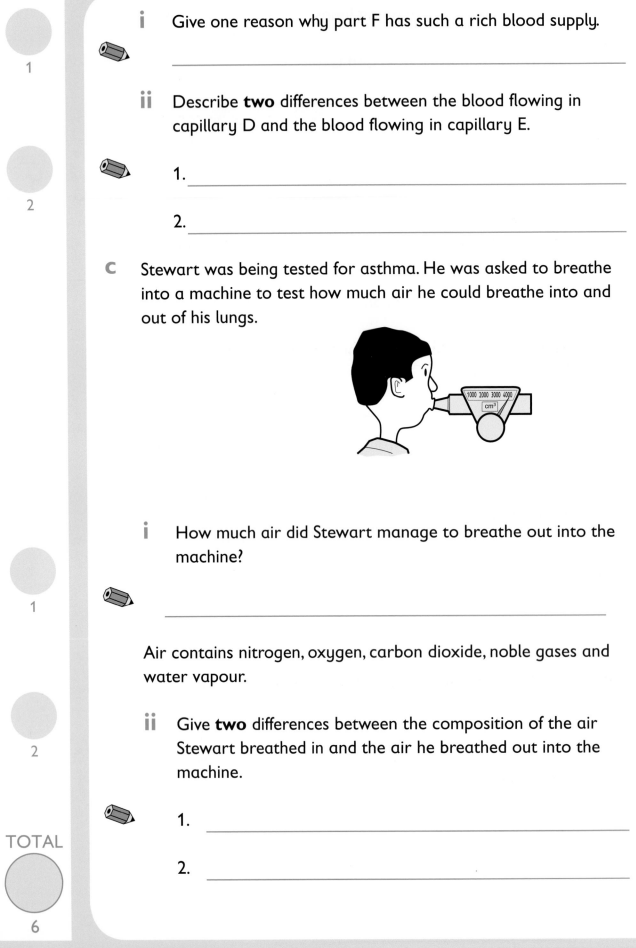

i   How much air did Stewart manage to breathe out into the machine?

1

_____

Air contains nitrogen, oxygen, carbon dioxide, noble gases and water vapour.

ii Give **two** differences between the composition of the air Stewart breathed in and the air he breathed out into the machine.

2

1. _____

TOTAL

2. _____

6

4 Some pupils were trying to explain particles to the rest of their class by acting out what the particles do.

Act 1:
The pupils slowly walked around the room, keeping in contact with each other.

Act 2:
The pupils ran around the room as fast as possible in all directions, sometimes colliding with each other and bouncing away.

Act 3:
The pupils stood closely packed together in neat rows all holding on to the person next to them.

a In which act are the pupils representing the particles in a gas?

_____

1

Explain your answer.

_____

_____

1

b In which act are the pupils representing the particles in a solid?

_____

1

Explain your answer.

_____

_____

1

TOTAL

4

1

c In which act are the pupils representing the particles in a liquid?

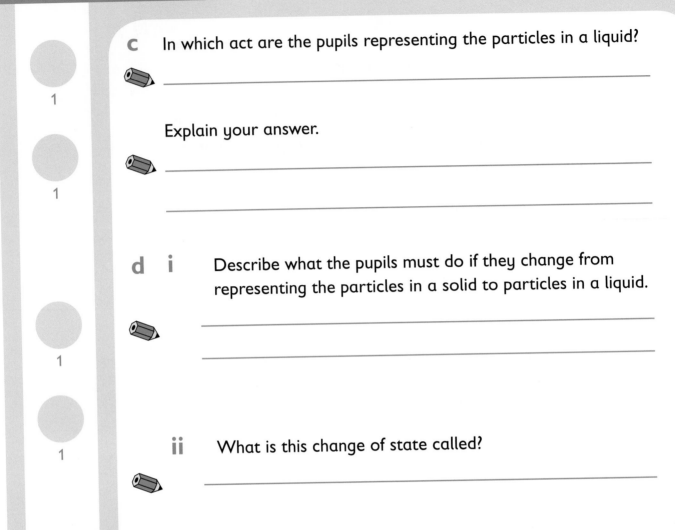
_____

1

Explain your answer.

_____

_____

d i Describe what the pupils must do if they change from representing the particles in a solid to particles in a liquid.

1

_____

_____

1

ii What is this change of state called?

_____

TOTAL

4

5 The diagram below shows an investigation to examine rusting.

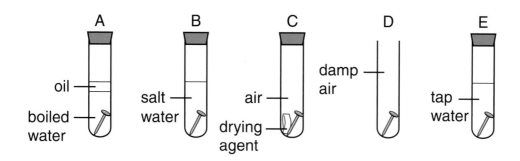

The table shows how each test tube was set up.

Tube	Treatment
A	A clean nail was covered with boiled water (to remove dissolved air) then the water was covered with a layer of oil.
B	A clean nail was added to salty water.
C	A clean nail was added to a tube with air in. A drying agent was added to dry the air.
D	A clean nail was added to a tube of air, which was left open.
E	A clean nail was added to tap water.

All the tubes were then left for 5 days.

a Which nail would you expect to be the most rusty after 5 days?

The nail in tube _____.

Explain your answer.

_____

_____

1

1

TOTAL

2

1

1

b Which nail would you expect to be the least rusty after 5 days?

The nail in tube _____.

Explain your answer.

_____

_____

2

c Suggest **two** factors that must be kept constant in order to make this investigation a fair test.

1. _____

2. _____

2

d i Metal objects can be protected from rusting in a number of ways.
Write down **two** ways in which the nails in the rusting experiment could have been treated to stop them from rusting.

1. _____

2. _____

1

ii Rust is an oxide of iron. Which of the following words describes the formation of rust from iron?

| condensation | reduction | oxidation | combustion |

TOTAL

7

_____

6a Which type of rock is formed from small pieces of other rocks settling in rivers, lakes, the sea or deserts?

✏ _____

1

b Which type of rock is formed by pressure and heat acting on other rocks?

✏ _____

1

c Which type of rock is formed when molten magma cools down?

✏ _____

1

d Give the name of one rock that has been formed from another.

✏ _____

1

e List four ways in which weathered rock can be carried away.

✏ i _____

ii _____

iii _____

iv _____

4

TOTAL

8

177

3

f The diagram below shows the size of crystals formed in three different places. For each one write down whether the cooling of the rock was slow, medium or fast.

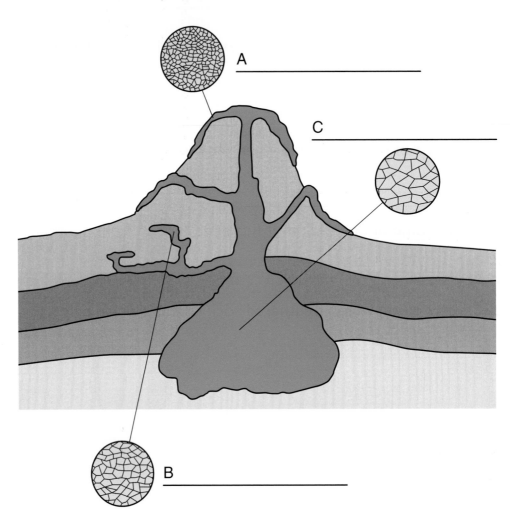

A _____

C _____

B _____

TOTAL

3

7

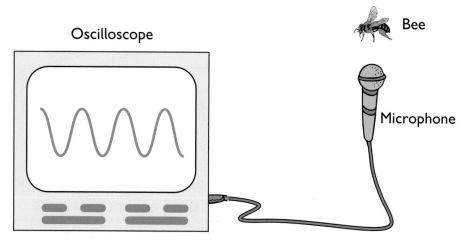

Oscilloscope

Bee

Microphone

Bees beat their wings many times per second. This is what makes the 'buzzing' noise when bees fly. A microphone can be used to record these 'buzzes' as the bee is flying at different speeds. The oscilloscope shows the sound as sound waves. Throughout the experiment the microphone and oscilloscope controls were kept the same. The results are shown below.

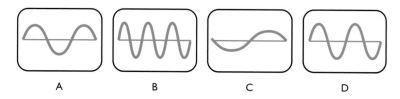

A   B   C   D

a Which one of the results shows the buzz from a bee flying at the fastest speed?

Explain your answer.

b Which one of the results shows the buzz with the lowest pitch?

Explain your answer.

1

1

1

1

TOTAL

4

179

c   The diagram below shows the pattern produced by a bee moving its wings at a rate of 20 beats per second.

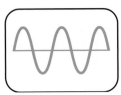

i   Draw on the diagram below the pattern that would be made by the bee moving its wings at twice the frequency.

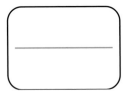

ii Draw on the diagram below the pattern that would be made by the bee moving its wings at the same frequency as above, but making a quieter sound.

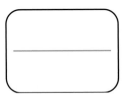

2

TOTAL

2

8 David and Freda are preparing to do a talk about energy sources. Imagine you are helping them.

a Present the data shown in the table below as a bar chart.

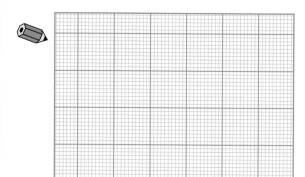

Energy resources	Estimated years of reserves
Coal	260
Gas	60
Oil	40
Uranium	25

3

b Why are fossil fuels called non-renewable energy resources?

_____

_____

1

c Look at this bar chart.

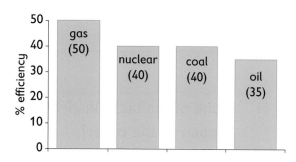

Calculate how many grams are wasted when one kilogram of each of the fuels is burned.

i Nuclear fuel _____   **ii** Oil _____

iii Gas _____   **iv** Coal _____

4

d List three examples of renewable energy sources.

i _____

ii _____

iii _____

3

TOTAL

11

9   Look at the circuit diagrams below.

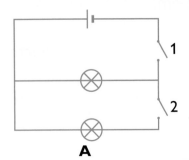
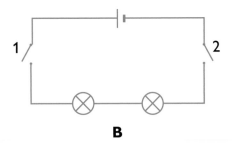

A   **B**

a   Which circuit has the bulbs connected in series?

   _____

b   The switches in the circuits are closed. The voltages of the cells in A and B are the same.

   i   In which circuit will the bulbs be brighter?

   _____

   ii   If one of the bulbs in circuit B was blown, what would happen to the other?

   _____

   iii   Describe what you would see in circuit A if switch 1 was closed and switch 2 was open.

   _____

   _____

1

1

1

1

TOTAL

4

The same circuits were set up again but this time ammeters were added and the switches removed. Ammeters are devices for measuring current. The units used are called amperes or amps (A).

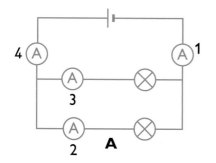

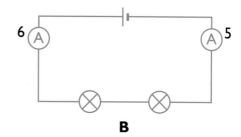

A   **B**

c i   Complete the table by writing in the correct number of amps.

   All bulbs are identical.

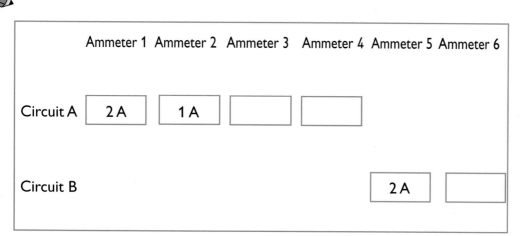

	Ammeter 1	Ammeter 2	Ammeter 3	Ammeter 4	Ammeter 5	Ammeter 6
Circuit A	2 A	1 A				
Circuit B					2 A	

3

ii   Explain your reasons for all three answers.

_____

_____

_____

2

TOTAL

5

10 The diagram shows part of a food web.

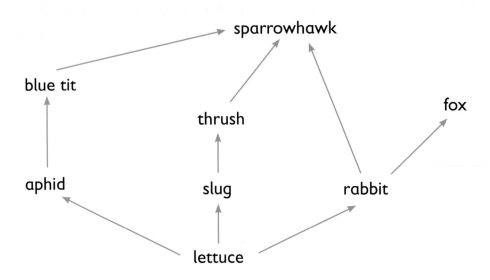

a Use **only** the information in the diagram above to answer the following questions.

Name **one** carnivore and **one** herbivore.

 carnivore _____

herbivore _____

b A predator is an animal that catches smaller animals to eat. Give the name of one predator and the name of one of its prey.

predator _____

prey _____

2

2

TOTAL

4

c If the number of rabbits in a particular habitat decreases, this affects the numbers of other animals living there. Use the food web to explain:

    i why the number of slugs might increase

_____

_____

    1

    ii why the number of foxes might decrease

_____

_____

    1

    iii why the number of thrushes might increase

_____

_____

    1

    iv why the number of thrushes might decrease.

_____

_____

    1

d The lettuce in the food web was sprayed with an insecticide. Explain why small amounts of the insecticide were found in the tissues of sparrowhawks.

_____

_____

    1

TOTAL

5

11 David has made some indicator using cabbage leaves. The indicator is a purple colour. When it is added to acids the indicator will turn red. When it is added to alkalis the indicator will turn blue.

a What colour would the indicator turn if added to the following substances?

Substance	pH	Colour of indicator
Lemon juice	4	
Detergent	11	
Vinegar	3	
Sodium hydroxide	14	

4

b What would be the pH value for a neutral substance?

_____

1

c Wasp stings are alkaline.
Which substance from the table above could you rub on a wasp sting to stop it hurting?

_____

1

Explain your answer.

_____

1

_____

TOTAL

7

186

d   Sometimes soil is too acidic to allow certain crops to grow.
A farmer may decide to add lime to the soil to make the soil less
acidic.

i   Is lime an acid or an alkali?

_____

_____

1

ii   Name the process of adding a substance to an acid to make
the pH 7.

_____

_____

1

TOTAL

2

187

12

a can of cold cola in a fridge

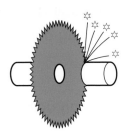

white-hot sparks from a cutter

a slab of iron glowing red-hot

freshly cooked beans on toast

a Each of the four objects shown above started at room temperature. Now they are all at different temperatures.

i Which object has lost thermal energy?

_____

1

ii Which object has had the largest gain in thermal energy?

_____

1

iii Which object is at the highest temperature?

_____

1

TOTAL

3

b Samantha puts a hot spoon into a glass of water. She leaves it for ten minutes.

i What will happen to the temperature of the water during the ten minutes?

_____

1

Explain your answer.

_____

_____

1

ii What will happen to the temperature of the spoon during the ten minutes?

_____

1

Explain your answer.

_____

_____

1

TOTAL

4

c Look at the table below. Column 1 shows the thermal energy stored in the spoon and the water before the experiment. Column 2 shows the thermal energy in the spoon and the water after ten minutes.

	Before	**After ten minutes**
Spoon	9800 J	6800 J
Water	4400 J	6800 J

i Calculate how many joules of energy the spoon loses during the ten minutes.

1

ii Calculate how many joules of energy have been gained by the water during the ten minutes.

1

iii Calculate the difference between the loss of energy from the spoon and the gain in energy by the water.

1

iv What has happened to the energy in part iii?

_____

_____

1

TOTAL

4

13

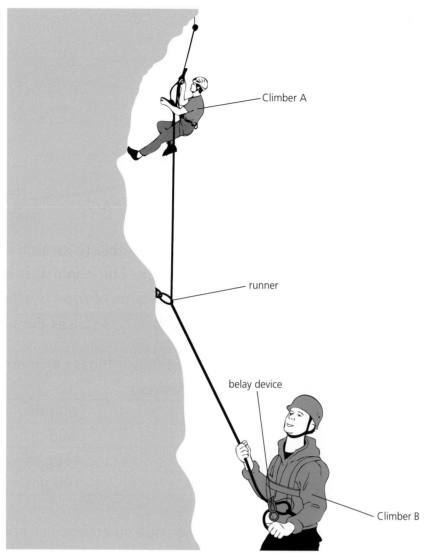

Climber A

runner

belay device

Climber B

Look at the diagram above.

a Name the force pulling Climber A down towards the ground.

_____

1

b Name the force that is helping Climber A to keep his feet on the rock.

_____

1

c Explain how Climber B is using this force to help to keep Climber A safe.

_____

_____

2

TOTAL

4

d

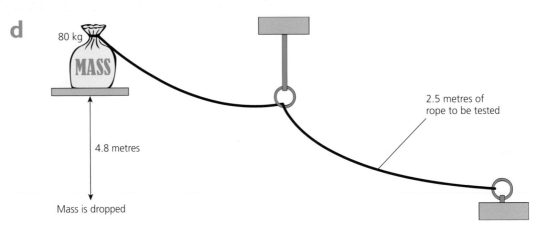

80 kg

MASS

4.8 metres

Mass is dropped

2.5 metres of
rope to be tested

Ropes for climbing need to be strong but also able to stretch to
reduce the shock on a climber if a fall occurs. The apparatus for
testing ropes is shown above. In tests 2.5 metres of rope is used.
The results of some tests are shown below.

	Stretch in metres	Number of falls before breaking	Mass per metre
Rope 1	1.0	12	60g/m
Rope 2	0.2	10	50g/m
Rope 3	0.0	2	150g/m
Rope 4	0.5	3	100g/m

i   Why is it important that a climbing rope stretches, but not
too much?

_____

ii A typical climbing rope is 50 metres long. How many grams
would Rope 3 be?

_____

iii To pass the international standard a climbing rope must not
break before it holds at least five falls of the 80kg mass.
Which two ropes pass the test?

Rope _____ and Rope _____

iv Which rope would you recommend a climber to buy?

_____

1

1

2

1

TOTAL

5

Question number	Answer	Mark
1a	An office worker will not be moving around as much and so will need less energy.	1
1b	Most 15-year-old girls have started menstruation and so will lose blood every month.	1
1c	15-year-old boys and girls are still growing and need calcium for bones.	1
1d	i. milk ii. chicken iii. celery	1 1 1
2a	reproductive system	1
2b	ovary	1
2c	oviduct *or* fallopian tube	1
2d	penis	1
2e	testicle	1
2f	sperm, fertilised, uterus, divides, embryo, placenta	6

3a	i. A = trachea
	   B = bronchus
	   C = alveolus
	ii. The alveoli increase the surface area of the lungs.
	iii. To strengthen the trachea and stop it from collapsing.
		3
		
		1
		1

3b	i. To let gases into and out of the blood. ii. 1. Blood in capillary D has more carbon dioxide. 2. Blood in capillary E has more oxygen.	1 2
3c	i. 4000 cm^3 ii. 1. The air he breathed in was richer in oxygen than the air he breathed out. 2. The air he breathed out was richer in carbon dioxide than the air he breathed in.	1 2
4a	Act 2 Particles in gases are free to travel at great speeds in all directions.	1 1
4b	Act 3 In solids the particles are tightly packed and held together.	1 1
4c	Act 1 In liquids the particles are close together but not as closely as in solids, they can flow.	1 1

Question number	Answer	Mark
4d	i. They must loosen their links and move a bit further away from each other but still be touching.	1
	ii. Melting	1
5a	B	1
	Salt makes things rust faster.	1
5b	A *or* C	1
	Rusting needs oxygen and water. Tube A has little oxygen in it. Tube C has little moisture.	1
5c	Temperature must be kept constant. Identical nails must be used.	2
5d	i. Any two from painting/oiling/coating with a more reactive metal such as zinc.	2
	ii. oxidation	1
6a	sedimentary	1
6b	metamorphic	1
6c	igneous	1
6d	One from marble, slate, coke, schist, gneiss.	1
6e	Four from water in rivers, wind, gravity, water in the sea, ice moving in glaciers.	4
6f	A = fast, B = medium, C = slow	3
7a	B	1
	The frequency (number of beats) is greater.	1
7b	C	1
	The amplitude of the waves is lower.	1
7c	i. There should be twice as many waves drawn as the diagram showing 20 beats per second, but waves remain same amplitude.	2
	ii. There should be the same number of waves but of a lower amplitude.	
8a	One mark for axis labelled, one mark for bars drawn to correct height, one mark for bars labelled.	3
8b	They are used up or they cannot be replaced because they take millions of years to form.	1
8c	i. 600 g ii. 650 g iii. 500g iv. 600 g	4
8d	Three from wind, waves, solar, geothermal, hydroelectric.	3
9a	B	1
9b	i. A	1
	ii. The other bulb would go out.	1
	iii. Only one bulb would light – the one nearest to the cell.	1

Question number	Answer	Mark

9c	i. Circuit A Ammeter 3 = 1 A
	                      Ammeter 4 = 2 A
	    Circuit B Ammeter 6 = 2 A
		3

	ii. The parallel circuit allows the two identical bulbs to share the current and so each branch will have 1 A. The current in the series circuit is the same throughout.	2
10a	sparrowhawk, fox, blue tit or thrush slug, aphid or rabbit	2
10b	predator: sparrowhawk, prey: blue tit/thrush/rabbit or predator: fox, prey: rabbit or predator: thrush, prey: slug or predator: blue tit, prey: aphid	2
10c	i. There will less competition for lettuce.	1
	ii. There will not be enough food to support the population.	1
	iii. More slugs could result in an increased population of thrushes.	1
	iv. Sparrowhawks might catch more thrushes as there are fewer rabbits.	1
10d	The insecticide was passed from lettuce to slugs then from slugs to thrushes and finally to sparrowhawks as the various living things were eaten. (Insecticide could also be passed from lettuce to rabbit to sparrowhawk.)	1
11a	Lemon juice red Detergent blue Vinegar red Sodium hydroxide blue	4
11b	7	1
11c	vinegar or lemon juice	1
	The acidic substance will neutralise the alkaline sting.	1
11d	i. alkali	1
	ii. neutralisation	1
12a	i. can of cola	1
	ii. slab of red-hot iron	1
	iii. white-hot sparks from a cutter	1
12b	i. It will rise.	1
	Thermal energy from the spoon will warm up the water.	1
	ii. It will fall.	1
	Thermal energy is lost to the cooler water.	1
12c	i. 3000 J	1
	ii. 2400 J	1
	iii. 600 J	1
	iv. It has been given out to the environment as heat.	1

Question number	Answer	Mark
13a	gravity	1
13b	friction	1
13c	Friction on the belay device. Friction on the runner.	1 1
13d	i. It should absorb the shock of the fall but not stretch enough to let the climber hit the ground. ii. 7500 g or 7.5 kg iii. Rope 1 　　Rope 2 iv. Rope 2	1 1 1 1 1

National Curriculum Levels

Science Test 2

Maximum marks: 120

Mark	0–40	41–61	62–75	76–100	101–120
Level	Below 4	4	5	6	7

Notes

Notes